Estill Voice Training
Level One
Figures for Voice Control
Workbook

Written by Jo Estill
Revised, Edited and Illustrated
by Mary McDonald Klimek
with Kerrie Obert
& Kimberly Steinhauer

Copyright © Estill Voice Training Systems International, LLC, 2005
Library of Congress Registration Number
ISBN 0-9764816-2-6
2010 Print Edition

Illustrations Copyright © Mary McDonald Klimek, 2005
Cover Design Concept: Michele Baker, Baker Creative
Interior Layout: Daniel Edward Klimek

Dedication and Acknowledgement

This book contains the latest evolution of Estill Voice Training®.

There would be no Estill Voice Training without the insight and perseverance of Jo Estill, singer, educator, and scientist. We gratefully acknowledge Jo Estill's vision of bringing scientific understanding and technical innovation to the teaching and rehabilitation of voice. She was the source of the Estill Voice Model and remains our inspiration.

Preparation of this text was a collaborative effort, with contributions from Certified Course Instructors and Certified Masters of Estill Voice Training.

Thanks to one and all who lent assistance.

TABLE OF CONTENTS

WELCOME!

Estill Voice International hopes that this learning experience will prove both powerful and rewarding. This course Workbook has been developed to assist in the process of learning Estill Voice Training®. The heart of this unique approach is the assumption that everyone has a beautiful voice. The balance of vocal health and aesthetic freedom is central to our teaching. Figures for Voice, the exercises that translate the theory of the Estill Voice Model into practical application, will provide course participants with the tools to achieve personal vocal goals and to discover the beauty in every voice.

Write in this book...

This is a *workbook*, not a text. It is to be used under the supervision of an Estill Mentor and Course Instructor or Estill Master Trainer – a teacher uniquely qualified to offer guidance. This teacher will expand upon this information. There are blank spaces provided for notes.

Practice, practice, practice...

Control of muscles, which is the essence of Estill Voice Training®, is not accomplished by reading, or even theoretical understanding – it is learned by doing, and doing, and doing. Be patient during this process, and know that this system is not absorbed into the body in the course of a few days, or even weeks. Practice is required for mastery. Working one-on-one with a teacher or in small practice groups is invaluable. Learn more by reading the Estill E-News (in your email inbox or on *www.estillvoice.com)*. Attend the Estill World Voice Symposium, held every other year. There are also additional materials from the **Think Voice Series** available for purchase on www.estillvoice.com: *Figures in a Flash* (flash cards containing the Figures and prompts), *Estill Etudes: Volume 1* (exercises with music); the "*Make & Move Larynx*" kit, and *Estill Voiceprint Plus*, a sound analysis program created specifically to be used while practicing Figures for Voice and loaded with pre-recorded samples in both male and female voices.

Take care of your voice...

Vocal health is *your* responsibility. Exercises in any course may hurt the voice if done incorrectly. Practicing without coaching and feedback from a certified Estill Voice Training® teacher and/or taking an exercise out of context may place the voice at risk.

Students should be in good vocal health. If an instructor has any concerns regarding the health of a student's voice – in a workshop, course, classroom, or studio – the teacher will refer that individual to a Laryngologist (an Ear-Nose-Throat doctor who specializes in the voice and larynx).

Estill Voice International wants everyone to have a long and healthy vocal life, however no claims or guarantees are made. Each individual is solely responsible for the health of his or her own voice.

Last, but not least: Have fun!

Learning to use the voice flexibly, in new and exciting ways, is very satisfying. Enjoy this experience.

We look forward to working with you.

COURSE INTRODUCTION

Introductory Exercise

Sing Happy Birthday, as a:

Party guest (Speech)

Innocent child (Falsetto)

Teasing bully (Belt/Twang)

Remorseful/repentant child (Sob)

"Proper" singer (Opera)

Guiding Principles of Estill Voice Training®

- Estill Voice Training® has no aesthetic bias
- All qualities are acceptable as long as vocal health is not jeopardized
- Everyone has a beautiful voice

Origins of Estill Voice Training®

Jo Estill, world-renowned educator, researcher, and singer, developed Estill Voice Training®. Although she started singing at a young age, lifted up onto the dining room table to sing for company, she often wondered, "*How am I doing this?*" When she left her performing career and went back to school for a Master's Degree in Music Education, she found some of the answers in course electives in the Speech and Hearing Department. As she learned about the anatomy and physiology of the head and neck (of the larynx, the ear, the vocal tract), and the principles of speech science (respiration, phonation, and resonance/acoustics), she began to acquire some of the answers to that long-standing question. Her inquisitive nature motivated a career move from performance to voice research and teaching. Her insights led to the development of the Estill Voice Model, the theoretical foundation for this approach to vocal training. Estill Voice Training®, also known as Estill Voice Craft, with its Figures for Voice, has been taught throughout the world. Jo Estill's achievements in voice research and teaching were recognized in 2004 with an honorary doctorate from East Anglia University.

The Estill Voice Model™ Evolved from Research

In 1981, X-Rays were taken of Jo Estill's vocal tract as she sang in four voice qualities. Changes were observed in the anatomical structures of the vocal tract that define its shape.

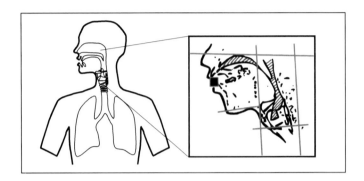

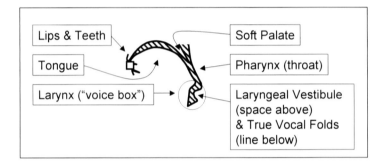

Conduct an Experiment – Sing "Happy Birthday" (as in the Introductory Exercise) and complete the following questionnaires:

Sing in SPEECH and describe:

The movement of the larynx?	None	Up	Down
The muscles surrounding the larynx?	Relaxed	Active	
The sensation of space in your larynx and throat?	Neutral	Large	Small
Tongue posture & space in the mouth?	Neutral	High Small	Low Large
Notice anything else?			

Sing in FALSETTO and describe:

The movement of the larynx?	None	Up	Down
The muscles surrounding the larynx?	Relaxed	Active	
The sensation of space in your larynx and throat?	Neutral	Large	Small
Tongue posture & space in the mouth?	Neutral	High Small	Low Large
Notice anything else?			

Sing in TWANG and describe:

The movement of the larynx?	None	Up	Down
The muscles surrounding the larynx?	Relaxed	Active	
The sensation of space in your larynx and throat?	Neutral	Large	Small
Tongue posture & space in the mouth?	Neutral	High Small	Low Large
Notice anything else?			

Sing in SOB and describe:

The movement of the larynx?	None	Up	Down
The muscles surrounding the larynx?	Relaxed	Active	
The sensation of space in your larynx and throat?	Neutral	Large	Small
Tongue posture & space in the mouth?	Neutral	High Small	Low Large
Notice anything else?			

Sing in OPERA and describe:

The movement of the larynx?	None	Up	Down
The muscles surrounding the larynx?	Relaxed	Active	
The sensation of space in your larynx and throat?	Neutral	Large	Small
Tongue posture & space in the mouth?	Neutral	High Small	Low Large
Notice anything else?			

Continue the experiment by comparing observations to X-Rays of Jo Estill singing in Speech, Sob, Twang and Opera. (from Colton and Estill, 1981)

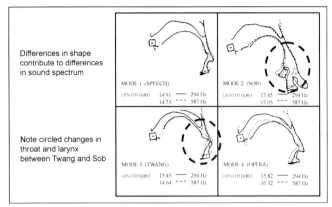

Differences in shape contribute to differences in sound spectrum

Note circled changes in throat and larynx between Twang and Sob

MODE 1 (SPEECH)
LENGTH (cm)   14.91 —— 294 Hz
              14.73 ---- 587 Hz

MODE 2 (SOB)
LENGTH (cm)   17.45 —— 294 Hz
              17.05 ---- 587 Hz

MODE 3 (TWANG)
LENGTH (cm)   15.45 —— 294 Hz
              14.64 ---- 587 Hz

MODE 4 (OPERA)
LENGTH (cm)   15.82 —— 294 Hz
              16.32 ---- 587 Hz

Notes

Estill Voice Training® Operating Principles:

- Knowledge is power; understanding how the voice works is a good thing
- Voice production begins *before* the voice is heard; muscle effort makes it happen
- The breath must be allowed to respond to what it meets on the way out
- Voice training is optimized when separated into 3 disciplines:
  Craft, Artistry, and Performance Magic

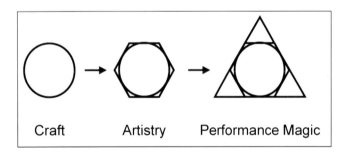

Craft   Artistry   Performance Magic

Notes

The Power-Source-Filter Model

- Breath (Power) draws true vocal folds (TVFs) into vibration
- True vocal fold vibration (Source) generates a pitch and overtones
- Vocal tract resonance (Filter) processes the frequency components of the voice into patterns recognized as vowels, consonants, and voice quality

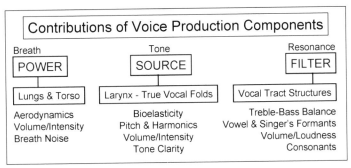

Notes

Estill Voice Training® Teaches Isolated Control of Individual Anatomical Structures within the Voice Production System

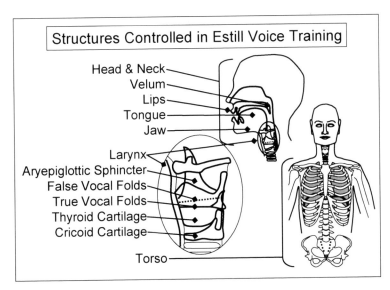

Overview of Voice Production Structures and Options in Level One

Larynx Structures

TVF Onset/Offset

Glottal Aspirate Smooth

TVF Body-Cover

Slack Thick Thin Stiff

False Vocal Folds

Constrict Mid Retract

Thyroid Cartilage

Vertical Tilt

Cricoid Cartilage

Vertical Tilt

AES

Wide Narrow

Notes

Vocal Tract Structures

Larynx

Low Mid High

Velum

Low Mid High

Tongue

Low Mid High Compress

Jaw

Forward Mid Back Drop

Lips

Protrude Mid Spread

Support Structures

Head & Neck

R	A

Relax Anchor

Torso

R	A

Relax Anchor

Structural Combinations and the Dynamic Nature of Voice Production

Combinations of structural conditions are used in speaking and singing. These habitual structural adjustments may have been acquired by trial and error or through years of training. Generally, conditions change between speaking and singing.

Voice quality is the characteristic of an individual voice or style of voicing, independent of speech sounds, pitch, and loudness. The term quality does not imply good or bad. In Estill Voice Training®, all voice qualities may be useful for a specific expressive purpose; however, vocal health always remains a priority.

The voice production system is dynamic and complex. The learning process is simplified by focusing on one structure at a time. Ultimately, Estill Voice Training enables the speaker or singer to differentiate and voluntarily control each structure to the extent that the biomechanical and aerodynamic nature of the system will allow. Dynamical Systems Theory (e.g. Kelso, 1995, and Wallace, 1996) describes the relationship that exists among the physical, environmental, and behavioral properties of motor (muscle and movement) control. Dynamical Systems Theory in voice production is evident in control of intensity during speaking and singing. For example, a speaker may instinctively take a larger breath to make a loud sound and a smaller breath to make a soft sound. The interaction between the respiratory and phonatory systems is what results in the change in volume. Dynamic principles apply to many other aspects of voice production and are integrated throughout Estill Voice Training®. The term *attractor state* is used in dynamical systems theory to describe a condition of stability during motor tasks. *Some* structures are naturally *attracted* to a specific condition at a given pitch or volume. For example, the condition of stability, or attractor state, for chest voice is low pitch, and the condition of stability, or attractor state, for head voice is high pitch. As the untrained singer moves up the scale in chest voice, the sound becomes unstable (voice cracks) and eventually gives way to a head voice at the higher pitches. The abrupt change of quality and conditions some singers experience between their chest and head voices is one example of attractor states in action. Attractor states are influenced by task, environment, training, and physical make-up (i.e., size of muscle, flexibility…). Attractor states can be modified with training. During the initial phase of training, movement away from an attractor state may cause a period of instability, but after deliberate and focused practice a consistent *new* attractor state can be established.

Levels of Study in Estill Voice Training®

Level One teaches **Figures for Voice Control**. The Figures for Voice, also called Compulsory Figures, or simply Figures, include isolation exercises for each of the structures previously discussed. On the next page is a blank Worksheet that provides yet another view of all the voice control options that will be presented in this Level One course.

Level Two introduces the **Figures Combinations for Six Voice Qualities**. This course focuses on Jo Estill's recipes and mixing instructions for six arbitrary modes: Speech, Falsetto, Sob, Twang, Opera, and Belt.

In Summary

The focus is on Craft
- Makes this approach useful for *everyone*: Speakers, Singers, Therapists, Teachers, Performers
- Lends itself to group learning, saving both time and money

In Estill Voice Training®, the student is empowered to make choices!

Knowledge of voice quality control...
- Reduces performance anxiety
- Provides confident use of the voice in vocally healthful manner
- Gives teachers and performers new vocal color choices

ESTILL VOICE TRAINING®
WORKSHEET

STRUCTURE OPTIONS

LEVEL ONE: Figures for Voice

OPTIONS	TVF1	FVF	TVF2	THY	CRI	AES	LARYNX	TONGUE	VELUM	JAW	LIPS	H&N	TOR
	glottal	constrict	slack	vertical	vertical	wide	low	low	low	forward	protrude	relax (R)	relax (R)
	aspirate	mid	thick	tilt	tilt	narrow	mid	mid	mid	mid	mid	anchor (A)	anchor (A)
	smooth	retract	thin				high	high	high	back	spread	relax (R)	
			stiff					compress*		drop		anchor (A)	

EFFORT DIAL — MIN / MAX

KEY TO ABBREVIATIONS

TVF1 = True Vocal Fold: Onset/Offset FVF = False Vocal Folds TVF2 = True Vocal Fold: Body-Cover THY = Thyroid Cartilage CRI = Cricoid Cartilage
AES = Aryepiglottic Sphincter H&N = Head & Neck TOR = Torso * = Advanced Option

8

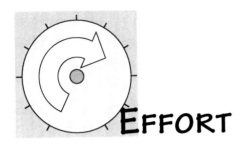

EFFORT

Introductory Exercise

Bring forefinger to thumb and maintain the lightest contact.

Press as hard as possible.

What kind of work is being done?

Where is it?

Was the breath held?

Press as hard as possible again, but *breathe* this time!

If the lightest contact is a 1 and the hardest is a 10, what would a 3 feel like?

How about a 7?

Notice the other fingers in the hand, the muscles of the arm and shoulder, and release the tension accumulating anywhere other than within the muscles of the lower arm required for this task.

Gradually increase the numbers (starting at 1, moving on to 2, and on up to 10), notice any uninvited muscle work, and release that tension as well.

> *Notes*
> _____
> _____
> _____
> _____
> _____
> _____
> _____

Anatomy & Physiology

Kinesthetic Perception

- Indicates *where* the muscles are working, and *how hard* they are working
- Perception of work, *Magnitude Estimation*, corresponds to objective measurements of that work, *Magnitude Production* (e.g., S.S. Stevens, 1957)
- Kinesthetic sense combined with the auditory sense helps to maximize voice motor control
- Effort is the voltage of the Voice Production System

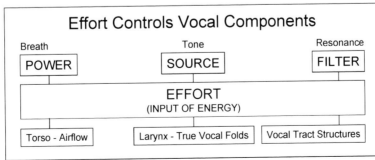
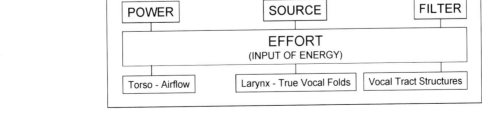

Guidelines for Monitoring Effort

- Locate the Effort
- Assign it a **Number**
- Hold the Number
- Perform the **Relaxation Maneuvers**

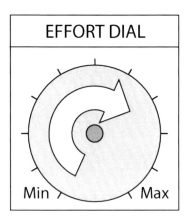

Relaxation Maneuvers

1) **Breathe,** to release tension in vocal folds
2) **Massage face, lips,** to release tension in facial muscles
3) **Walk briskly,** to release tension in breathing muscles
4) **Roll tongue around teeth**, to release tension in tongue
5) **Chew,** to release tension in jaw
6) **Make short, soft vowels,** to release tensions associated with voicing
7) **Speak normally,** to release tensions associated with speech
8) **Sing an / ŋ / ("ng" in English),** to release tensions associated with singing
9) **Add music or monologue,** to release tensions associated with complex vocal tasks

Rules for Monitoring Effort in Vocalization

- Maintain most-comfortable-vocal-effort (MCVE) at the level of the true vocal folds
- Distinguish vocal trauma from muscle ache
- Listen harder to the muscles than the voice
- No Figure is mastered until all extraneous tensions have been released
- Monitoring Effort requires constant attention
- Hold the Number to the end of the breath

Always listen harder to the muscles than the voice!

The Relaxation Maneuvers ask for short, soft vowels so that the perception of the sound of the voice does not overpower the perception of how hard the muscles are working, the Number. In learning and practicing Figures for Voice™, try some of the training exercises, and the Figures themselves, in silence. Silent practice is often revealing, and has the further advantage of conserving the voice.

Notes

_____

_____

_____

_____

_____

Training Exercises

Locating and quantifying Effort

1) Shake the hand of someone.
2) Isolate the effort in the hand clasp (eliminate extraneous movements).
3) Assign an Effort Number to your hand clasp.
4) Reveal the Numbers of both partners.
5) Take turns being the active partner in this exercise, and demonstrate different Numbers: 1, 7, 5, 9...

A mental inventory of activity in individual muscles will be required to acquire control of the vocal tract structures.

Partners in this exercise will likely have different strengths of grip, *Magnitude Production*, for the same Number, *Magnitude Estimation*. This is perfectly fine. Indeed, during mastery of a given structure, the correspondence of Magnitude Production and Estimation will change. Remember how much Effort it took when first learning any activity – sewing a hem, playing the piano, riding a bike?

The amount of work invested today as an Effort Number of 10 will likely come to feel easier over time, and will then be assigned a lower Number.

Holding a Number and
Performing the Relaxation Maneuvers

1) Protrude the lips, hard. Use an 8 or 9 for your Effort Number.
2) Hold this Number, and perform each of the Relaxation Maneuvers.
3) Monitor the Number closely, and recover if it changes from task to task.

Notes

The Value of Effort

Voice production begins before the voice is heard

Muscle Effort is a more reliable guide than listening. Once the voice is heard it is too late to change it. It cannot be called back for revision. Furthermore, internal hearing (which includes input from bone conduction of sound) clouds aural perception.

Working the muscles is satisfying

Effort will make high intensity singing and speaking feel easy.
Effort is also the key to avoiding laryngeal constriction.

POWER

Introductory Exercise

Take a deep breath.
Is the breath being held, and if so, where?
Exhale…
How did you exhale?
Where was the locus of Effort during *inhalation*?
What was the Number?
Where was the locus of Effort during *exhalation*?
What was the Number?
Did the Effort stay in the same locus throughout the inhalation, throughout the exhalation?

> *Notes*
> _____
> _____
> _____
> _____
> _____

Breathing is Dynamic

Dynamic systems *change*: they do not operate in exactly the same manner under all conditions. The respiratory system is a good example. The same muscle-pattern-routines are not used to pump breath in and out of the lungs day in and day out. Think of the contrast in the breath patterns for resting and running to catch a train before it leaves the station! Consider the changes in the rate of inhalation and exhalation, in the amount of air moving in and out of the lungs, and in the location of muscle activity. Posture can also affect breathing. Quiet breathing will change for sitting, standing, and lying down. The brain and body are adept at making these adjustments.

Breathing can be Involuntary or Voluntary

In most physical states, breathing is naturally governed by the involuntary nervous system, as lung volume and rates of inhalation/exhalation adjust to maintain oxygen levels in the blood. During speaking and singing, breathing is regulated by the *voluntary* nervous system to varying degrees. In the service of a long musical phrase, the singer's voluntary control of the exhalation overrides the natural biological imperative to inhale. This prompted Jo Estill to coin the phrase, "Singing is an Unnatural Act!" Under some conditions, so is speaking!

Anatomy & Physiology

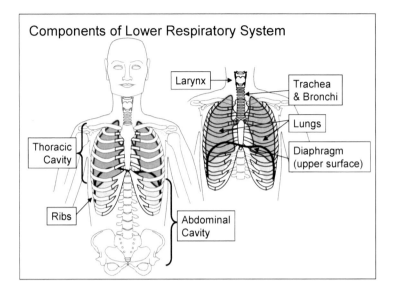

Components of Lower Respiratory System

- Larynx
- Trachea & Bronchi
- Lungs
- Diaphragm (upper surface)
- Thoracic Cavity
- Ribs
- Abdominal Cavity

Respiratory Function of the Larynx

The larynx must remain open for breathing to occur. It closes to protect the lungs.

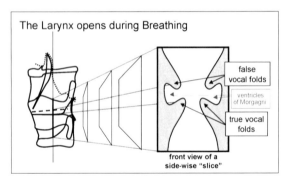

The Larynx opens during Breathing

- false vocal folds
- ventricles of Morgagni
- true vocal folds

front view of a side-wise "slice"

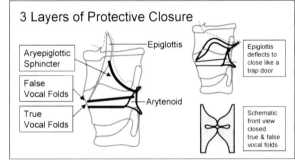

3 Layers of Protective Closure

- Aryepiglottic Sphincter
- False Vocal Folds
- True Vocal Folds
- Epiglottis
- Arytenoid
- Epiglottis deflects to close like a trap door
- Schematic front view closed true & false vocal folds

Notes

Inhalation & Exhalation

The lungs are spongy and passive. Lung volume is determined by the space available within the thorax. Respiratory muscles affect the size of the thorax and are divided into 2 categories:

Inhalatory – these muscles tend to be *active* during inhalation and create *more* space for the lungs. Increased lung volume creates negative air pressure (within the lungs), and breath flows in. The primary muscles of inhalation are the diaphragm and external intercostal (between-the-rib) muscles.

Exhalatory – The simple release of contraction in the diaphragm and external intercostals is sufficient to create *less* space in the thorax, increase air pressure, and create the outward flow of breath. Flow will continue until the Resting Expiratory Level (REL) is reached, a physiological balance point where pressure within the lungs equals the pressure in the atmosphere. At REL, neither inhaltory nor exhalatory forces are at play. If exhalation is to continue, different muscles must be engaged. The primary muscles of this further exhalation are the internal intercostal muscles and the muscles of the abdomen. These muscles tend to be *passive* when lung volumes are still above REL, *active* when lung volumes are below REL.

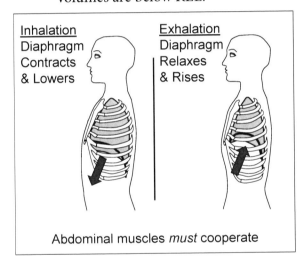

Inhalation
Diaphragm
Contracts
& Lowers

Exhalation
Diaphragm
Relaxes
& Rises

Abdominal muscles *must* cooperate

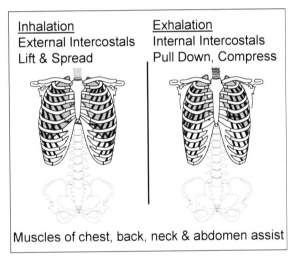

Inhalation
External Intercostals
Lift & Spread

Exhalation
Internal Intercostals
Pull Down, Compress

Muscles of chest, back, neck & abdomen assist

Notes

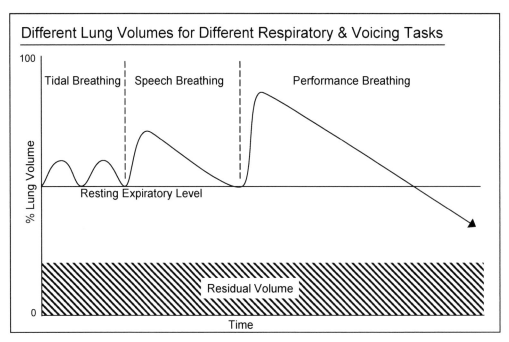

Recoil breaths and respiratory attractor states

A **recoil breath** may occur when lung volume is low. Increasing activity of the muscles of exhalation literally *squeezes* more breath out of the lungs. This activity compresses the rib cage and displaces abdominal contents upwards, lifting the diaphragm. When this exhalatory effort is released, the ribs spring up and the diaphragm drops down, creating an abrupt increase in lung volume with a negative air pressure that draws the air in, before the individual has time to think about it. Recoil is a term that describes this sensation of breath rushing in without having to actively breathe.

Generally, individuals can be sorted into 2 categories: **belly breathers** who experience abdominal expansion/contraction during breathing, and, **chest breathers** who experience a rise/fall in the chest and sometimes even the shoulders. Belly breathing is useful for some singing styles and speaking situations; chest breathing is useful in others. The point is that neither one is right or wrong. They are simply individual respiratory attractor states.

Notes

16

Training Exercises

Exercise in the influence of lung volume on the direction of the breath

1) Take a comfortable breath (increase lung volume), and simply let go of the inhalatory effort.
What happened? Exhalation.

2) Squeeze all your breath out (decrease your lung volume), and then let go of the squeezing effort.
What happened? Inhalation.

If exercise 1 was done with Low Effort, then the body probably returned to a respiratory balance point where all the muscles were at rest in a "neutral" position, Resting Expiratory Level (REL).
If exercise 2 was done with High Effort, the following inhalation was probably spontaneous, and would be described as a "recoil breath."

Exercise in the influence of lung volume on Effort in breath holding

Hold the breath with lung volumes at, above, and below Resting Expiratory Level (REL).
Each time, ask the following questions:
What is the Effort Number within the larynx?
Is there muscle Effort elsewhere? If so, what is its Number?

1) Find Resting Expiratory Level, and hold the breath.
2) Exhale below REL and hold the breath.
3) Take in a small breath to a lung volume above REL and hold it.
4) Take a larger, yet still comfortable breath above REL and hold it.
5) Take a *huge* breath, filling the lungs, and hold it.

What did you observe?

Notes

Exercise in the influence of lung volume on Effort in voicing

Notice the Effort in the larynx and breathing muscles while producing a soft (so you can "hear" your muscles) / i / ("ee" in English):

1) At REL
2) Below REL
3) After a small inhalation above REL
4) After a medium inhalation above REL
5) After a huge inhalation above REL

What did you observe?

Notes

_____

_____

_____

_____

_____

_____

_____

_____

_____

_____

_____

_____

_____

Application Discussion

There is no Compulsory Figure for Breath in the Estill Voice Model, nor is there one correct way to breathe.

Each individual may employ a specific muscular pattern during quiet breathing, or speech. This pattern would be called the attractor state for breathing: the tendency to localize respiratory movement in the shoulders, chest, or abdomen that is the personalized *habit* while breathing.

Some attractor state breathing patterns will serve well for particular speaking and singing tasks; others will not and will need to change.

The breath must be allowed to adjust to what it meets on the way out.

Source and Filter can have feed-back and feed-forward effects on breathing patterns. Certain structural conditions will trigger changes in the experience of the breath.

PITCH

Introductory Exercise

Observe Effort for a pitch-glide through your range on an / ŋ /, as if forming the end of the word "sing" in English (see box below for explanation of this symbol):

> How high did you go?
> How low did you go?
> Was the vocal tone consistent or variable?
> Did the voice have breaks or gear shifts?
> Where in the range were pitches produced with low Numbers, high Numbers?
> What was the breath Effort in different regions of the range?
> Did the breath change for the ascending or descending glide?
> Did the eyebrows rise for the high notes, and did the chin press down for the low?

As we learn the various Figures for Voice™ we will return to this exercise, solving such problems as may have been encountered.

Notes

The symbol / ŋ / comes from the **International Phonetic Alphabet** (IPA), in which there is a single symbol for each speech sound (or phoneme) in all the languages of the world. In this case, the sound is the "ng" sound of English. Letters or symbols from the IPA will appear between two forward slashes.
The following are other IPA symbols you will find in this text

/ i / = see, meet, feet in English	/ o / = the first component of the American English diphthong in boat, tote
/ ɪ / = sit, hit, mitt	
/ e / = the first component of the American English diphthong in fate, bait	/ u / = blue, moon
/ a / = father	/ æ / = fat, hat in American English
	/ ŋ / = sing, song
	/ j / = yes, yawn

Anatomy & Physiology

Tone Production Basics

Tone is produced by the interaction of the breath and the true vocal folds.
Cycles per second and frequency of vibration both correspond to pitch.
Pitch is the perception of vibratory frequency.

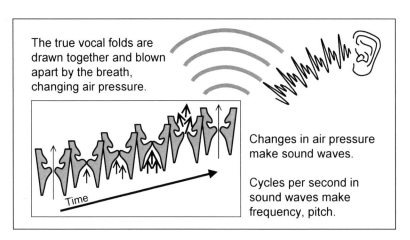

The true vocal folds are drawn together and blown apart by the breath, changing air pressure.

Time

Changes in air pressure make sound waves.

Cycles per second in sound waves make frequency, pitch.

Estill Voiceprint Plus

Analyze range using a piano or record the voice in the *Estill Voiceprint Plus* computer program in Spectrogram/Practice mode.
Visual cues for this exercise:

- In a black & white display, the lowest and darkest trace on the screen is the Fundamental Frequency, or pitch of the tone
- The parallel lines above are overtones, or harmonics

Place the cursor at any point along the lowest pitch trace and the frequency will be shown in the "Frequency Display" box at the bottom of the screen.

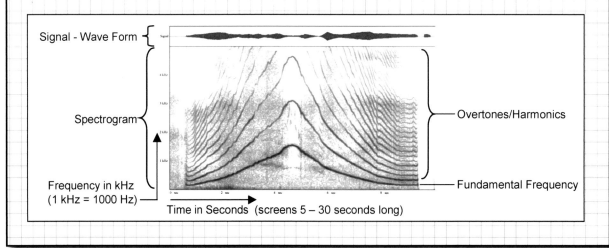

Signal - Wave Form

Spectrogram

Frequency in kHz (1 kHz = 1000 Hz)

Overtones/Harmonics

Fundamental Frequency

Time in Seconds (screens 5 – 30 seconds long)

Pitch Production in the Voice is a Dynamic Process

Physics tells us that length, mass, and tension can influence frequency. This model works well for musical instruments with strings. The voice follows laws of physics, but the biomechanics and aerodynamics of the voice are complex and dynamic. The vocal folds are multi-layered and can adjust to vibrate in several different ways at any single pitch. As wind instrument players know, breath can also influence pitch.

There are attractor state adjustments in the breath and true vocal fold mass, tension, and length for different regions of the total pitch range that support some of the definitions proposed for vocal registers: fry (creak), chest voice (modal), head voice, and falsetto. Attractor states in voice motor control can explain the balance between biomechanics and aerodynamics at different pitches in the range that results in different voice qualities being more easily produced in one region of the range than another.

Voice breaks result from the abrupt gear shifts between these attractor states.
Figures for Voice™ will enable the vocalist to choose whether or not to accept the attractor state or create new attractor state/s through training. The terms register, head voice, and chest voice are *not* part of the Estill Voice Model™.

Pitch Production Basics

In very simple terms, the true vocal folds are short at low pitches, long at high pitches.
The thyroarytenoid (TA) and cricothyroid (CT) are the intrinsic muscles of the larynx that regulate the length of the true vocal folds.
Intrinsic muscles are those that run between any of the laryngeal cartilages.

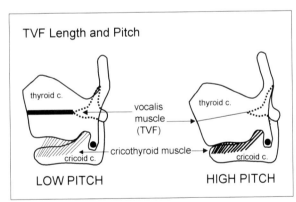

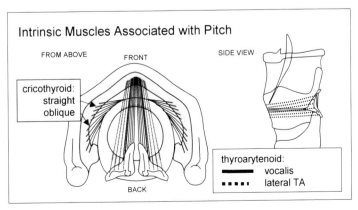

Notes

_____

_____

_____

_____

_____

_____

Extrinsic laryngeal muscles (that run from the cartilages of the larynx to other structures) can also become involved. For example, the larynx may rise or fall in the neck respective to moving higher or lower in the pitch range. These changes in larynx height affect the length and width of the throat (pharynx), thus altering the Filter (vocal tract) to better resonate high or low frequencies. They may also assist the thyroarytenoid and cricothyroid to adjust for the extremes of the range. The muscles attaching to the hyoid bone from above and below affect larynx height/vocal tract length predictably, except for the thyrohyoid. Although an infrahyoid muscle, it can act as an elevator

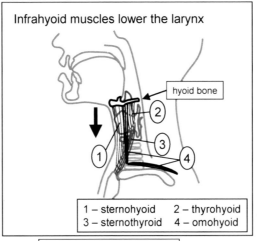

Infrahyoid muscles lower the larynx

hyoid bone

1 – sternohyoid   2 – thyrohyoid
3 – sternothyroid   4 – omohyoid

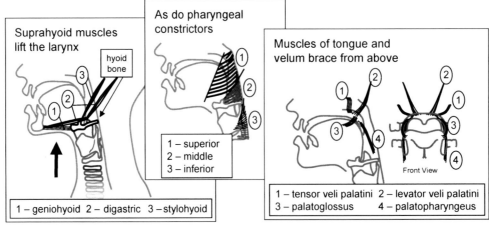

Suprahyoid muscles lift the larynx

hyoid bone

1 – geniohyoid 2 – digastric 3 – stylohyoid

As do pharyngeal constrictors

1 – superior
2 – middle
3 – inferior

Muscles of tongue and velum brace from above

Front View

1 – tensor veli palatini 2 – levator veli palatini
3 – palatoglossus   4 – palatopharyngeus

Training Exercises

Exploring Effort for pitch through the range

On an / ŋ / as in "sing":

1) Match random pitches played on a keyboard, or simply jump between various pitches throughout the range. (If not using a keyboard, *think* the pitch before producing it.)

Or

2) Siren a simple song on an / ŋ / as in "sing." Sing from note to note very slowly and breathe as needed.

With either exercise, note the location/s of Effort and the Effort Number/s for each note.
When does the larynx adjust for each new pitch?
What happens to the Number/s as a pitch is sustained?
What happens to the Breath?

Monitor for the spread of Effort during this exercise, keeping the sound soft and performing all of the Relaxation Maneuvers.

Notes

Application

There are many important observations about Effort in Pitch Production:
- Pitch is prepared in the musculature of the larynx and vocal tract *before* the tone is made
- The location of Effort at the high and low ends of the range will be different
- Effort numbers associated with pitch production are going to be lower in the middle of the range, and higher at the extremes of the range
- Beware! Sometimes the Effort required to produce a high/low pitch closes the larynx down! This is called laryngeal constriction.

Each Compulsory Figure is designed to be practiced "on any pitch." To avoid constricting the larynx when first learning the Figures, keep the pitches of your practice within a comfortable Effort range.

Pitch gliding is often called sirening. If there were voice breaks or gear shifts during these pitch exercises, if the range was not as high or as low as expected, patience is advised. There are Compulsory Figures ahead that will solve these problems. Later in the course there is a specific exercise to extend the pitch range called The Siren.

TRUE VOCAL FOLDS: ONSET/OFFSET

Introductory Exercise

Say each of the following aloud, and then repeat it several times, but *silently*:

"Uh-oh!"
"Hey!"
"You!"

What did you *feel* and *hear* each time?

Notes

Anatomy & Physiology

In this Figure, two muscular activities are coordinated:

- The movement of the true vocal folds (TVFs) into position for vibration
- The beginning of exhalation

The muscles that attach to the arytenoid cartilages open and close the true vocal folds. The space between the true vocal folds is called the *glottis*.

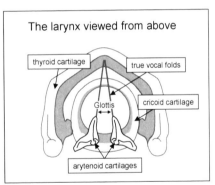

The larynx viewed from above

thyroid cartilage — true vocal folds — cricoid cartilage — Glottis — arytenoid cartilages

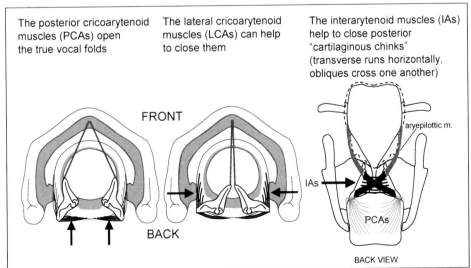

The posterior cricoarytenoid muscles (PCAs) open the true vocal folds

The lateral cricoarytenoid muscles (LCAs) can help to close them

The interarytenoid muscles (IAs) help to close posterior "cartilaginous chinks" (transverse runs horizontally, obliques cross one another)

FRONT

BACK

aryepilottic m.

IAs

PCAs

BACK VIEW

The Three Conditions

Icon	Condition & Description	Schematic	Hand Signal
↑	**Glottal** TVFs close (1) before exhalation begins (2)		
↑	**Aspirate:** *Abrupt, Gradual* Exhalation begins (1) before TVFs close (2) *abruptly* or *gradually*		
↑	**Smooth** Exhalation and TVF movement occur *simultaneously*		

Notes

Estill Voiceprint Plus

When practicing this Figure with the *Estill Voiceprint Plus* program (Practice & Spectrogram Settings), look for the following visual cues:
- Glottal – sharp vertical edge in both spectrogram and wave signal, harmonics start with dark horizontal lines
- Aspirate Abrupt – step-wise increase/decrease in wave signal, scatter of breath noise prior to abrupt vertical start of harmonic traces
- Aspirate Gradual – gradual expansion/contraction of wave signal after initial rise; gradual emergence of harmonic traces from the scatter of noise
- Smooth – gradual expansion/contraction of the wave signal, with gradual emergence of harmonic traces, and not all at once

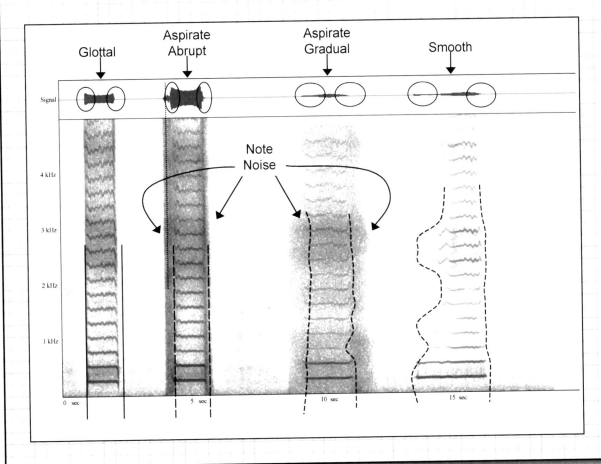

Training Exercises

Reminder:

Always begin practice at MCVE (Most Comfortable Vocal Effort). This may mean practicing with a favorite vowel and in the easiest pitch range. After the Figure for False Vocal Fold Control has been introduced, the range may be expanded.

Glottal Onset

1) Close the true vocal folds (hold breath for an instant) then say/sing an / i / at a comfortable pitch.
   Hear the distinct sound that occurs at the beginning of the tone as the true folds gently burst apart and into vibration. The burst should be no greater than a simple "uh-oh." In fact, say, "uh-oh!"
   Feel the Effort levels associated with this onset.
   See the vertical line of this Onset in the spectrogram.

2) Try Glottal Onsets on other vowels: / e, a, o, u /.

3) Practice Glottal Onsets across the range:
   Beginning at the bottom of an octave scale in the middle of the range, sing up through the scale on an / i / using a glottal onset on each tone.
   Repeat with other vowels, / e, a, o, u /.

Aspirate Abrupt Onset

1) Blow into an / i / vowel. Hold the true vocal folds apart as the breath begins, then allow them to be abruptly pulled together. There will be a pop-like sound. Compare/contrast Glottal and Abrupt Aspirate onsets and feel how different they are.
   Hear the noise of breath prior to the

Notes

pop of tone onset.

Feel the Effort levels associated with this onset.

See the vertical emergence of harmonics from the scatter of breath noise in spectrogram.

2) Try Aspirate Abrupt Onsets on other vowels: / e, a, o, u /.

3) Practice Aspirate Abrupt Onsets across the range:
Beginning at the top of an octave scale (comfortably high) and on the vowel / i /, keep the folds open for as long as possible, blow and pop down the scale, tone by tone. Repeat on other vowels.

Aspirate Gradual Onset

1) Sigh into the tone, feeling the breath moving before the sound begins. Blow into the / i /, but do not just let the true vocal folds pop together – move them *slowly* into the breath stream.

Hear the noise of breath prior to the gradual emergence of tone.

Feel the Effort levels associated with this onset.

See the staggered emergence of harmonics from noise in spectrogram.

2) Try Aspirate Gradual Onsets on other vowels: / e, a, o, u /.

3) Practice Aspirate Gradual Onset across the range:
Starting at a comfortably high pitch, on the vowel / i /, descend the scale starting each tone "on" the breath. Control the closing of the true vocal folds: don't let them pop.

Notes

Smooth Onset

1) Say, "you." This word begins with the glide / j / (the "y" sound in English). Say the / j / silently and continue in an / i /.

   Or

   Take a comfortable inhalation, and at the initiation of exhalation, bring the TVFs into position for vibration. Some voice teachers and therapists call this putting the onset at the top of the breath.

   When this onset is produced correctly it will feel like "drinking in the tone" – another common prompt for this onset.

   Hear how smoothly and easily the tone emerges.

   Feel the Effort levels associated with this onset.

   See the absence of noise and the staggered emergence of harmonics in spectrogram.

2) Try Smooth Onsets on these vowels: / e, a, o, u /.

3) Practice Smooth Onsets across the range:

   Try this onset on these different vowels up and down a comfortably pitched scale.

   The sound should be devoid of:
   - the *edge* of the Glottal Onset
   - the *pop* of the Abrupt Aspirate
   - the *breathiness* of the Gradual Aspirate

Practice of Offsets:

The exercises above can be repeated with the conditions at the *end* of the tone. As the use of Offsets is heavily influenced by musical style, these exercises may be practiced in the context of work with Voice Qualities in Level Two.

Notes

Figure for True Vocal Fold: Onset/Offset Control

Demonstrate the following Onsets and Offsets:

1) Glottal: closure precedes/ends airflow

2) Aspirate Abrupt: abrupt movement in/out of airflow

3) Aspirate Gradual: gradual movement in/out of airflow

4) Smooth: movement and airflow coordinated simultaneously

Perform these tasks on / i, e, a, o, u /, at any pitch.
Practice different Onset/Offset combinations.
Practice with different True Vocal Fold: Body-Cover conditions.

Note: When first learning this Figure, do not attempt to practice with *all* of the True Vocal Fold: Body-Cover conditions and on *every* pitch in the range. Stay within a most comfortable vocal effort range (MCVE). Once the Figures for True Vocal Fold: Body-Cover and False Vocal Fold Control and the various Efforts required to access the total range have been mastered, this Figure can be practiced on a more advanced level.

Application

Note that movement of the true vocal folds and the movement of breath can be controlled independently and coordinated in different ways.

Also note that Onsets can influence the tone that follows. This is part of the dynamic nature of voice production.

Know that any Onset *can* be used to initiate a tone in any True Vocal Fold Body-Cover condition. This is another demonstration of independent control, a skill acquired as Craft is mastered.

Sample Application Exercise: Try singing "Happy Birthday" with different Onsets. Replace the consonant at the start of each note with one of the 4 Onsets. Repeat the process with the remaining Onsets. Does the choice of Onset change the voice quality? Simply observe – once again there is no right or wrong answer to this question.

FALSE VOCAL FOLDS

Introductory Exercise

Have a good stretch.
Or...
Grab the seat of your chair
and try to 'lift' yourself up!

What is happening in the larynx?
What is happening to the breath?

Notes

Anatomy & Physiology

There are 3 levels at which the larynx can open/close

- The aryepiglottic sphincter
- The false vocal folds
- The true vocal folds

The larynx closes at different levels in different activities

The larynx closes at the bottom two levels:

- During thoracic (chest) fixation (bracing), a natural action in preparation for strenuous activity such as lifting heavy objects, defecating, or childbirth -- this kind of closure also occurs when you prepare to fight, flee, or scream
- In preparation for throat clearing or coughing, to increase lung air pressure

During normal voicing, variable laryngeal closure occurs at the lowest level alone (variable in that the true vocal folds both close *and* open during the vibratory cycle).

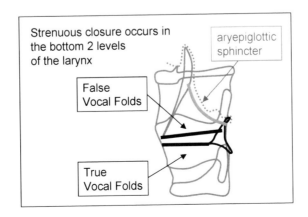

Strenuous closure occurs in the bottom 2 levels of the larynx

aryepiglottic sphincter

False Vocal Folds

True Vocal Folds

The false vocal folds can open/close while the true vocal folds are approximated (in position to vibrate)

There is a continuum of positions for the false vocal folds during voicing: the closing observed in straining, the mid-range position associated with Most-Comfortable-Vocal-Effort (MCVE) spoken voice, and the opening associated with the natural activities of laughter and crying.

Closure of the false vocal folds during voicing, even slightly inward from the mid-range position, can affect both breath flow and the vibration of the true vocal folds. Both speaker or singer *and* listener will perceive the tone as strained or pressed.

The muscles that close the true and false vocal folds in sphincteric (a circle of closure) manner are thought to be primarily intrinsic (muscles that attach to any two cartilages of the larynx). (Review diagrams for True Vocal Folds: Onset/Offset).

The muscles that allow the FVFs to be opened and closed independently of the TVFs have not been identified, but may include *extrinsic* muscles of the larynx.

Extrinsic laryngeal muscles attach at one end to any of the cartilages of the larynx and at the other end to the hyoid bone or sternum, or from the hyoid upwards to attachments within the head.

Notes

The Three Conditions

Icon	Condition & Description	Schematic	Hand Signal
	Mid The FVF position of comfortable speaking/ singing, mid-way between squeezed shut and widely opened.		
	Constrict The condition when the FVFs are moved inward from Mid and toward their closed position.		
	Retract The condition when the FVFs are moved outward from Mid to a widely opened position.		

Estill Voiceprint Plus

When demonstrating or practicing this Figure with the *Estill Voiceprint Plus* program (Practice & Spectrogram Settings), look for the following visual cues:

- Mid – clear harmonics, some interharmonic noise
- Constrict – increased interharmonic noise, irregular harmonic traces
- Retract – minimal interharmonic noise, smoother harmonic traces

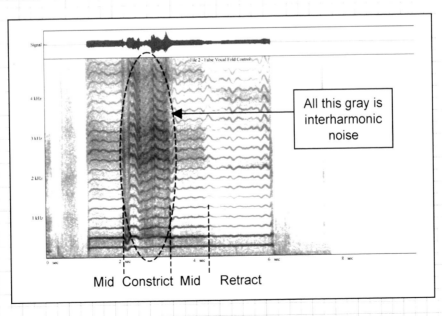

Training Exercises

Opening and closing the 2 lower levels of the larynx at the same time

1) Breathe quietly. The true and false vocal folds are open.
   - What do you feel?
   - Where is the Effort?
   - What is its Number?
2) Hold the breath. The true and false vocal folds are closed.
   - What do you feel?
   - Where is the Effort?
   - What is its Number?

Effortful closing and opening

1) Grunt silently as though lifting something very heavy.
   The true and false vocal folds are constricted.
   - What do you feel?
   - Where is the Effort?
   - What is its Number?
2) Laugh or cry/sob silently.
   The true and false vocal folds are retracted.
   - What do you feel?
   - Where is the Effort?
   - What is its Number?
   Hold that Number and perform the Relaxation Maneuvers.

Sustained Retraction of the False (and True) Vocal Folds with "Laugh Posture"

1) Laugh "silently" through the "hee-hee-hee" of a cartoon or comedy character, making a wheeze-like noise in the roof of the mouth from the turbulence of the air between the tongue and hard palate.
2) Hold the position of the "hee" and laugh *all* the air out of the lungs. When exhaling far below Resting Expiratory Level, what happens during

Notes

the inhalation? A recoil breath, a gasp?

3) Release the tongue from the "hee" and hold the high Effort Number of "hard laughter" while exhaling as much air as possible. This time, hold the Effort Number beyond the exhalation and inhale with the "recoil breath."

4) Breathe comfortably, in and out, through this high Number "laugh posture."
   - What do you *feel*?
   - What do you *hear*?

You should hear nothing!

Try the following experiment:
- Plug your ears and breathe with a relaxed larynx, no Effort, Mid FVFs
- Plug your ears with your fingers and breathe in and out through high Number "laugh posture"

Under the Mid condition, air turbulence will occur – possibly less of it during the inhalation, when the vocal folds tend to actively abduct, or open. Practice the high Number "laugh posture" until you the noise of breathing is eliminated. Remember the experience of the location of this Effort, and use it in the exercises that follow.

2 degrees of Constriction and Retraction while exhaling (without tone)

1) Constrict lightly (low Number) and begin to exhale, as though whispering "he." Then suddenly Retract to a low Number laugh/cry condition for the remainder of the exhalation.
   - What do you *feel*?
   - What do you *hear*?
   - What do you *see* in the spectrogram?

Notes

2) Repeat the previous exercise, but with high Effort Numbers in both the Constricted and Retracted conditions. What are your Numbers?
- What do you *feel*?
- What do you *hear*?
- What do you *see* in spectrogram?

2 Degrees of Constriction and Retraction while voicing

1) Constrict lightly while saying / i /. After holding the constriction for a short period of time, suddenly Retract, using a low Number laugh/cry posture.
- What do you *feel*?
- What do you *hear*?
- What do you *see* in spectrogram?

Try this exercise on other vowels: / e, a, o, u /.

Practice it on other pitches.

2) Repeat the exercise above, but with high Effort Numbers in both the Constricted and Retracted conditions.
- What do you *feel*?
- What do you *hear*?
- What do you *see* in spectrogram?

Try this exercise on other vowels: / e, a, o, u /.

Practice it on other pitches.

Notes

Figure for False Vocal Fold Control

1) Demonstrate these conditions of the Vocal Folds:
   Open vs Closed   Constricted vs Retracted
2) Demonstrate without tone:
   2 Effort levels of FVF Constriction and Retraction
3) Demonstrate with tone:
   2 Effort levels of FVF Constriction and Retraction
4) On a vowel, the following sequence:

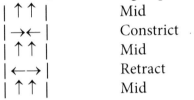

| ↑↑ | Mid
| →← | Constrict
| ↑↑ | Mid
| ←→ | Retract
| ↑↑ | Mid

Perform these tasks on / i, e, a, o, u /, at any pitch.
Practice moving between conditions abruptly, gradually.
Practice with different True Vocal Fold Body-Cover conditions.

Application

Singing and Speaking are "Unnatural Acts."
Many common situations in speech and song can trigger FVF Constriction, for example:
- ends of phrases (holding back the breath)
- high intensity voice qualities, such as Opera and Belting (strenuous vocal activities)
- emotionally challenging entrances (due to stage fright or due to exposure)
- high notes, low notes (strenuous vocal activities)

As the naturally de-constrictive or *Retracting* property of laughter and crying is engaged, the triggers for Constriction are overcome. Active Retraction of the False Vocal Folds is obligatory in the voice qualities that tend to trigger constriction: Twang, Opera and Belting. It is built in to Sob. Mid FVF condition in Speech or Falsetto is acceptable – as long as pitch or intensity does not trigger Constriction.

Maintaining Retraction all the time is a choice, but it colors the voice in a way that may make it sound unnatural. In some vocal styles, where a natural sound is prized, Mid and even Constricted FVFs will be required some/all of the time. If performing in such a style, monitor the Effort of breath very carefully to avoid scratching.

Application Exercise: Return to the Exercise for Pitch Control and at the extremes of the range Retract to a high Number. This may solve the cutting out at the top phenomenon and extend the range.

TRUE VOCAL FOLDS: BODY-COVER

Introductory Exercises

Say/sing an / i / loudly.
Say/sing an / i / softly.
Now, start loud and suddenly go soft.
Now, start soft and suddenly go loud.
 What do you feel in the larynx?
 What do you feel in the breath?
Use an Aspirate Abrupt onset and simply
"blow" into an / u /, sung or spoken.
Make the sound of a creaky door.
 What do you feel in the larynx and breath
 with these sounds?

Notes

Anatomy & Physiology

Conditions required for TVF vibration

True vocal fold vibration occurs when the TVFs are adducted (brought together) near
the mid-line of the larynx with the edges close enough for the breath stream to suck them
together and then blow them apart (Bernoulli's Principle).

Conditions for tone production

When the TVFs are closing or closed, air pressure builds up beneath them – subglottal
(below-the-glottis) air pressure. When the TVFs open, subglottal air pressure drops.
The air pressure changes that occur as a result of TVF vibration make the sound waves that
resonate within the vocal tract and propogate into the space around the speaker/singer.

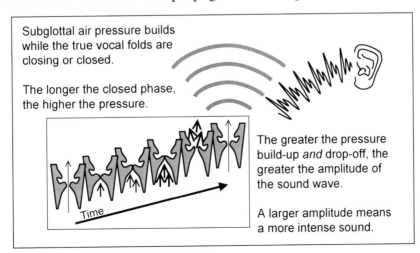

Subglottal air pressure builds while the true vocal folds are closing or closed.

The longer the closed phase, the higher the pressure.

Time

The greater the pressure build-up *and* drop-off, the greater the amplitude of the sound wave.

A larger amplitude means a more intense sound.

The extent to which the true vocal folds close, and the length of time that they remain closed will influence subglottal pressure (the pressure below the true vocal folds). The amount of pressure that builds is directly related to the intensity or volume of the vocal tone.

The cycles per second of these sound waves make the Fundamental Frequency or pitch of the voice. Because the cycling of vibrations/sound waves is regular (or *periodic*), harmonics are also produced. Harmonics are whole number multiples of the Fundamental, also called *overtones* or *partials*.

The structure and mechanics of the true vocal fold edge

There are 4 layers of cells in the edges of the TVFs, which make them appear differently from other structures in the respiratory system. Most people are surprised by their whiteness. Each layer has a different biomechanical property. The complexity of the TVF edge is part of what allows humans to voice with such an extraordinary range of vocal colors, timbres, or qualities. A useful model that describes how these layers interact with each other and function during vibration is called the the "body-cover model of fundamental frequency control" (e.g., Hirano, 1977; Titze, 1988), hence the name of this Figure.

The deepest layer is the vocalis bundle of the thyroarytenoid muscle. Like other muscles in the body, it can be soft and pliant when relaxed, hard when contracted. It can be shortened or stretched, bunched up or pulled taut, and *with* or *without* isometric contraction at any length.

The next two layers of tissue (intermediate and deep lamina propria) comprise the vocal ligament. It is elastic, and its flexibility will vary with both length and the status of the muscle just beneath it.

The vocalis and vocal ligament form the **body** of the true vocal fold.

The superficial lamina propria is a soft gel-like layer of cells. The epithelium of the true vocal fold edge is a mere 4-6 cells thick. Together, these 2 layers comprise the **cover**.

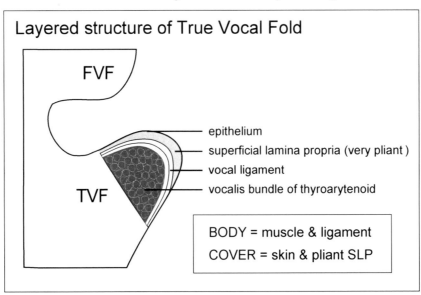

Layered structure of True Vocal Fold

FVF

epithelium
superficial lamina propria (very pliant)
vocal ligament
vocalis bundle of thyroarytenoid

TVF

BODY = muscle & ligament
COVER = skin & pliant SLP

Mucosal wave

Under certain conditions of vocal fold vibration, the edge of the true vocal folds deforms in such a manner that there is a fluid wave visible, rippling through the cover and possibly deforming body as well, from the lower border of the edge upward and then out to the side over the superior surface of the true vocal fold. This mucosal wave is produced *within* the tissue of the true vocal folds – not in the mucous secretions that lubricate them.

Mechanics of modes of vibration

The different vibratory modes of the true vocal folds can be explained by Dynamical Systems Theory. The complex mechanical interplay of **body** and **cover** as the length of the true vocal folds changes (via contraction of the thyroarytenoid and/or cricothyroid), together with the aerodynamic influence of the breath, results in different vibratory modes, gears or registers. Within this "dynamic system" are those attractor state vibratory modes that are most recognizable – for example, Modal/Speech and Loft/Falsetto. In Estill Voice Training®, the challenge is to learn how to maintain the conditions that produce a given vibratory mode *beyond* the frequency boundary of its attractor state.

Notes

The Four Conditions

Icon	Condition & Description	Hand Signal
	Slack Recognized as glottal fry, or creaky voice. Both body and cover are loose. This Body-Cover combination results in a unique vibratory pattern producing pulses of sound energy.	
	Thick Known as the modal or speech register. The true vocal folds are relatively short, with some contraction/muscle tone in the vocalis muscle within the body. The cover is pliant, and the folds ripple (mucosal wave) from the lower border to the upper border of the fold edge, with a *thick* depth of contact through the cycle.	
	Thin May occur naturally at higher pitches where the vocal folds are elongated, and/or during soft voicing. Less cover flexibility and/or less breath result in vibration without the lower-to-upper ripple, a *thin* or shallow depth of contact.	
	Stiff May occur naturally at higher pitches where the vocal folds are elongated, pulled taut, and positioned slightly away from the midline. In some individuals, this may be accomplished by cricothyroid activity; in others, the arytenoids may rock back, raising the back end of musculomembranous portion of the true vocal folds. Known as falsetto in Estill Voice Training, there is little or no contact during vibration, although the tone may or may not be breathy.	

Notes

Schematic drawings of these conditions:

Time	→					
Slack						repeats irregularly
Thick						repeats regularly
Thin						repeats regularly
Stiff						repeats regularly

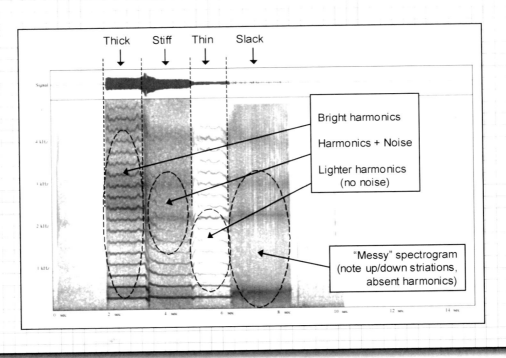

Estill Voiceprint Plus

When demonstrating or practicing this Figure with the *Estill Voiceprint Plus* program (Practice & Spectrogram Settings), look for the following visual cues:
- Thick – larger waveform, dark harmonic traces, some interharmonic noise
- Stiff – increased interharmonic noise that may create a "blurry" spectrogram
- Thin – smaller wave signal, lighter harmonics, minimal interharmonic noise
- Slack – vertical striations, no horizontal harmonic lines

Training Exercises

Slack

1) Make a creaky door sound on an / a /. Shift back and forth between Slack folds and a regular speaking tone (Thick folds).
    What is going on with the breath?
    What do you *feel* in the larynx?
    What do you *see* on the spectrogram?

2) Try Slack folds on these vowels:
    / i, e, o, u /.

3) Practice Slack folds through a comfortable *speaking* range:
    A low pitch will *facilitate* Slack folds; so does low breath Effort.

Note: Slack folds also facilitates FVF Constriction, particularly higher in the range. For this reason, we recommend practicing Slack folds only within the comfortable range of the speaking voice. We find it useful, recognizing that those who train and rehabilitate the voice disagree about its value and risks.

Thick

1) Say a *loud* / i /. Sustain the / i / at that pitch, singing it.
    Use a Glottal Onset to facilitate Thick folds.

2) Try Thick folds on these other vowels:
    / e, a, o, u /.

3) Practice Thick folds across the range. Starting at the low end of your range, sing on / i / up through an octave scale using Thick folds.
    Use a Glottal Onset on each tone.
    Retract the FVFs |←→|, if you feel Constriction.

Note: There is a point in your range where this Thick condition is no longer comfortable (where the vocal folds are

Notes

drawn to an *easier* attractor state). The ultimate point of this exercise is to be able to maintain all the conditions for Thick folds throughout the entire range. Beyond the break, the tone produced in this vibratory mode weakens. By accepting the challenge and discomfort (both in what you feel and what you hear), and by allowing the tone to become smaller -- less volume -- while ascending, it will be possible to sustain Thick folds into the upper pitches of the range. Go as high as possible. Subsequent Figures will provide enhanced control.

Do not use more breath to equalize the volume while ascending the scale; it may produce a break into Stiff folds and/or trigger FVF Constriction.

Thin

1) Say or sing a loud / i /, say or sing a soft / i /. Sustain the soft / i /.
   Use a Smooth Onset to facilitate Thin folds.

2) Try Thin folds on other vowels: / e, a, o, u /.

3) Practice Thin folds across the range Beginning at a comfortably high pitch, sing down an octave scale on / i /, using a Thin folds. Use a facilitating Smooth Onset on each tone.

Stiff

1) Hold the thumb on the lower lip and blow an / i /, as if blowing across the neck of a little bottle. Use an Aspirate Abrupt Onset to facilitate Stiff folds. Try to maintain the same Stiff fold adjustment, but with less breathiness in the tone.

Notes

2) Try Stiff folds on these other vowels: / e, a, o, u /.

3) Practice Stiff folds across the range. Because the TVFs are already stretched and stiffened somewhat at higher frequencies, begin on a comfortably high pitch and sing an / i / with Stiff folds on each step of a descending scale. Use a facilitating Aspirate Abrupt Onset on each scale step.

Note: As this vibratory mode is taken lower in pitch, into the range where it is not an attractor state, invest more Effort in sustaining thc condition. Again observe that the tone weakens when it passes this boundary. Allowing for this fact, Stiff folds will readily descend the scale. Using more breath in attempt to equalize the volume while descending, may cause a break into Thick folds.

Notes

Figure for True Vocal Fold: Body-Cover Control

On a vowel, demonstrate the following TVF: Body-Cover conditions:

1) Begin with **Thick** folds, change to **Thin** folds
2) Begin with **Thin** folds, change to **Thick** folds
3) Begin with **Stiff** folds, change to **Thin** folds
4) Begin with **Thin** folds, change to **Stiff** folds
5) Begin with **Thick** folds, change to **Stiff** folds
6) Begin with **Stiff** folds, change to **Thick** folds
7) Begin with **Thick** folds change to **Slack** folds
8) Begin with **Slack** folds, change to **Thick** folds

Practice these tasks on / i, e, a, o, u /.
Practice moving between conditions abruptly, gradually.
Perform tasks 1 – 6 on any pitch; 7 & 8 in mid-low range.

Application

In figure skating, the conceptual source of Figures for Voice™, control of the edges of the skate blade is critical in all aspects of performance. Control of the vocal fold edges are every bit as important to singers and speakers.

Control of TVF: Body-Cover will contribute to:
- consistent quality throughout the range (avoiding breaks)
- consistent loudness through the range by *change* of TVF: Body-Cover condition
- planned voicing breaks ('cracking' with emotion, yodeling)
- sudden intensity changes for dramatic/musical effect
- changes in intensity to preserve the stress patterns of words in songs

Application Exercise: Return to "Happy Birthday," as sung in Onset practice, only this time, consciously control the TVF: Body-Cover that follows the Onset, using Glottal to Thick, Aspirate to Stiff, or Simultaneous to Thin. Lower the key, and add some Slack. Try singing the lyrics with consonants restored while maintaining a Thick, Thin, or Stiff TVF: Body-Cover condition throughout the song. Remember, this is only an exercise. Once Craft is mastered, *any* Onset can precede *any* TVF: Body-Cover. Take another song and experiment with the effects created by *changing* Body-Cover condition from note to note, or even within a single note.

THYROID CARTILAGE

Introductory Exercise

"Meow" high, soft, like a kitten whimpering.
Or
"Whimper" on an / ŋ / like a puppy or dog.

Place the fingers over the larynx and prepare to make either of these sounds. Where is the Effort?

"Meow" or "whimper" while descending a scale, maintaining all of the numbers.

What do you feel?
What do you hear?

Notes

Anatomy & Physiology

The thyroid cartilage is connected to the cricoid cartilage at the cricothyroid joint. The two cartilages can rotate relative to each other along the axis of the cricothyroid joint. There is a space between the lower edge of the main body of the thyroid and the arch of the cricoid, called the cricothyroid space. This space can be opened or closed. These 2 conditions influence True Vocal Fold: Body-Cover condition.

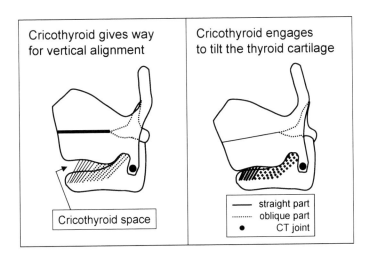

As was felt in the whimper preparation, the cricothyroid muscle does not always work alone.

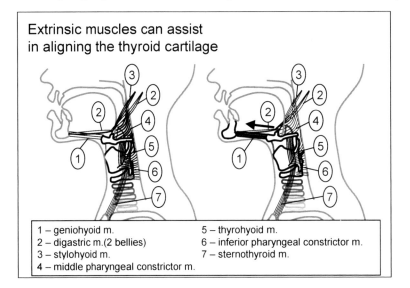

Extrinsic muscles can assist
in aligning the thyroid cartilage

1 – geniohyoid m.
2 – digastric m.(2 bellies)
3 – stylohyoid m.
4 – middle pharyngeal constrictor m.
5 – thyrohyoid m.
6 – inferior pharyngeal constrictor m.
7 – sternothyroid m.

The Two Conditions

Icon	Condition & Description	Schematic	Hand Signal
	Vertical The condition of the thyroid cartilage in quiet breathing.		
	Tilt The condition when the cricothyroid muscle is actively engaged and the thyroid cartilage is rotating forward.		

Notes

52

Notes

Estill Voiceprint Plus

When demonstrating or practicing this Figure with the *Estill Voiceprint Plus* program (Practice & Spectrogram Settings), look for the following visual cue:
- The Tilted condition will have a marked reduction in interharmonic noise

This reduction in noise is likely the source of our perception of sweetness in this condition.

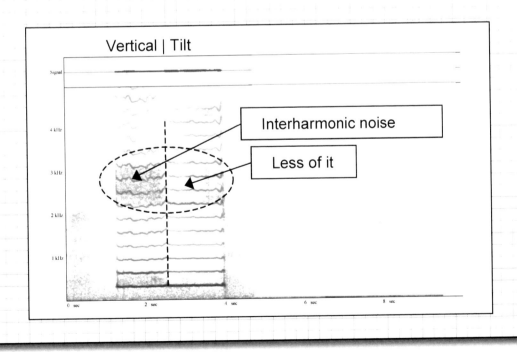

Training Exercises

Finding the crico-thyroid space (C-T space)

There should be an indentation or a space between the thyroid and cricoid cartilages, referred to as the crico-thyroid space, "C-T space" for short. To find it, feel for the bump of the thyroid notch and slide down, or feel for the bump of the cricoid arch and slide up.

Vertical Thyroid

1) Relax the musculature surrounding the larynx and breathe quietly.
   What do you feel in the C-T space and higher up?
   This should be the Vertical Thyroid Cartilage condition.
   Assign it a Number.
2) Say or sing / i / with a Vertical Thyroid Cartilage.
3) Say or sing other vowels, / e, a, o, u / with Vertical Thyroid Cartilage.
4) Start at a comfortably low pitch and sing up the scale, on / i /, maintaining this Vertical Thyroid Cartilage posture.

Thyroid Tilt

1) Whimper on / ŋ / or "meow" at a relatively high pitch.
   What do you feel?
   What do you hear?
   This should be the Tilted Thyroid Cartilage condition.
   Assign this Effort a Number, hold it, and perform the Relaxation Maneuvers.

Notes

2) Say or sing / i / with Thyroid Cartilage Tilt. If using a high Effort Number, the folds may already be thin.
3) Say or sing some other vowels, / e, a, o, u /, with Thyroid Cartilage Tilt.
4) Start at a comfortably high pitch and sing down the scale, on / i /, maintaining the Tilted Thyroid Cartilage condition.

Thyroid Cartilage control independent of TVF: Body-Cover

1) Say or sing / i / with Thick folds and Vertical Thyroid Cartilage.
2) Add Thyroid Cartilage Tilting, but monitor carefully to keep the Thick fold condition.
   What do you *feel*?
   What do you *hear*?
   There should be a "sweetening" of the tone *without* a change of TVF: Body-Cover condition.
3) Repeat with other vowels, / e, a, o, u /.
4) Repeat steps 1, 2, and 3 with Thin folds, and then with Stiff folds.

Notes

Figure for Thyroid Cartilage Control

On a vowel, demonstrate the following Thyroid Cartilage conditions:

1) Begin with Vertical and change to Thyroid Tilt.
2) Begin with Thyroid Tilt and change to Vertical.

Perform these tasks on / i, e, a, o, u /, at any pitch.
Practice moving between conditions abruptly, gradually.
Practice with different True Vocal Folds: Body-Cover conditions.

Application

Holding the Thyroid Cartilage in a Vertical or Tilted condition is another way to influence True Vocal Folds: Body-Cover. This becomes important under pitch conditions that might naturally move the cartilages into a different postural relationship with one another. For example, Effort to maintain Thyroid Cartilage Tilt may help an operatic singer avoid the shift to a speech-like chest voice in the low range. Maintaining a Vertical Thyroid Cartilage may help a Pop or Musical Theatre singer to stay in speech-like quality when singing in mid to upper range.

Many singers, in any number of musical styles, add a bit of Thyroid Cartilage Tilt to a note as they hold it, "sweetening" the tone. With this sweetening sometimes comes vibrato.

Thyroid Cartilage Tilt can be used to "sweeten" any voice quality, even belting.

A bit of extra effort in Thyroid Tilt will also enhance the upper range. This principle is employed in the Estill Siren, an exercise for controlling pitch throughout the range. If some of the top notes are still missing, the Siren may help recover them.

THE SIREN

The Siren - Exercise for Finding the Range

On an / ŋ / as in / Iŋ /, Siren as high and as low as possible.

To produce the particular recipe for a Siren, use Thin TVF: Body-Cover, a High Tongue, a Tilted Thyroid Cartilage, FVF |←→|, and maximum Effort. At the highest pitches in the range, use as hard a feeling of Effort in the head with as soft a sound as possible in the larynx. The Siren should move from the lowest to highest pitches in the range without any break or roughness and no change of quality.

Training Exercises

Pretend you are a child with a toy fire truck that has no siren

1) Siren on an / ŋ /, noting that the tongue and the velum allow no sound to pass through the mouth.
2) Make sure the tongue is positioned for the / ŋ / of "sing" rather than "song," to keep the tongue high and not too far back in the mouth.
3) Go as high and low as possible.

For this exercise, keep the TVF: Body-Cover Thin by using Effort in Thyroid Tilt, particularly in the low range where Tilt does not come "naturally."
Invest a higher number of both Thyroid Tilt and FVF Retraction at the top of the range.
Did the range expand?

Notes

Isolate the awareness of muscles working to establish pitch in silent practice

1) While exhaling, silently Siren the whole range.
2) Stop and hold the sensation of the highest note, the lowest, and several in between.
3) Hear the pitch in the mind and come as close to actually making the sound as possible, remaining silent.

Miren

What's Mirening? Forming the words in the mouth while Sirening a song.
(Mouth + Siren = Miren.)
Miren a simple song.
Mirening demonstrates independent control of the front and back of the tongue, and can be used to release the jaw during singing – regardless of the pitch.

Learning a new song

1) Siren the song to establish the muscle memory for the melody.
   (Remember that FVF retraction |←→| is part of the Siren recipe.)
2) Miren the words, to "program" the memory of the lyrics.
3) Extract the vowel in each syllable, each note.
4) Siren from note to note, very slowly, and:
   - Hold the Effort for the Siren at that pitch while breathing in
   - Sing the pitch and vowel with the desired TVF: Onset and Body-Cover condition

Once all of the Figures have been learned, add Effort in other structures to pre-set *all* of the elements required for the voice quality chosen.

Notes

CRICOID CARTILAGE

Introductory Exercise

Shout out a "Yay!" (happy, excited!).
Or
Pretend you are Italian, and shout out an / e /
("ay!") with a Glottal Onset.

What did you hear?
What did you feel?
    In the breath...
    In the larynx...
    In the crico-thyroid space?

Notes

Anatomy & Physiology

There is a set of attractor state structural conditions for shouting, a natural human activity that can serve as an expression of joy, excitement, warning, or anger. A Narrow Aryepiglottic Sphincter is one of those conditions, as are a High Larynx and Cricoid Tilt.

The crico-thyroid joint that allowed for the closing down of the C-T space during Thyroid Cartilage Tilt can also be rotated for an opening *stretch* of the cricothyroid membrane.

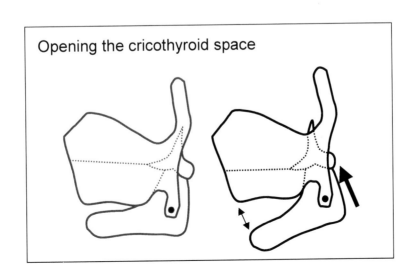

Opening the cricothyroid space

As with the muscular mediation of False Vocal Fold Retraction, the action that accomplishes this shift in cartilage alignment is not anatomically obvious. The cricopharyngeus division of the inferior pharyngeal constrictor may play a role. These muscle fibers run from the front of the spine to the sides of the cricoid. As with other structures studied, this muscle would have to be aided by secondary muscles attaching to the hyoid bone and thyroid cartilage to succeed in opening the C-T space. This action would explain the experience of a downward tug on the larynx during shouting, even though the larynx is clearly high in the neck.

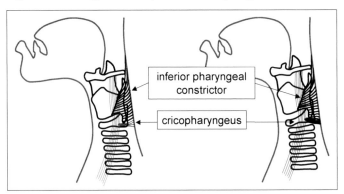

An alternative physiological strategy

There is another physiological possibility: the thyroid cartilage could rock *backwards* on the ends of its lower horns, opening the C-T space.

The middle pharyngeal constrictors and supra hyoids, or even the thyroarytenoids could pull back on the thyroid cartilage for this option, which might explain the head-thrown-back position some people use when they shout, assisting the up and back action on the hyoid bone and thyroid cartilage.

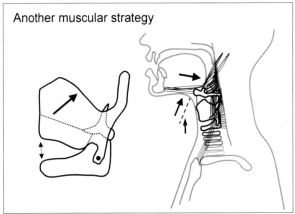

Cricoid Tilt increased loudness with less breath

One common misconception about how the voice works is that more breath *must* be used to make a louder voice. The functions of shouting require that a very loud noise be produced as quickly as possible. A deep breath would slow the process down. Clearly, another physiological solution is employed.

Remember that air pressure changes make sound waves. Making the respiratory apparatus work harder will not necessarily make the vocal sound bigger. There is a complex and dynamic interplay of Power and Source in shouting. The longer the true vocal folds remain closed during each vibratory cycle, the more intense the glottal source tone can become. In context of shouting, the introduction of Cricoid Tilt makes Thick folds *thicker* resulting in a very long closed phase. In belting, the true vocal folds remain closed for 70% of each vibratory cycle. For the shouter/belter, this increased sub-glottal air pressure is generated *without* the perception of additional airflow. Indeed, increased movement of breath (as in the common misconception of pushed breath for belt-voice production) will tend to blow the true vocal folds *open*, dropping the pressure. Production of a high intensity sound like shouting (and belting) with increased breath Effort will almost certainly trigger FVF Constriction to help hold the TVFs closed long enough to make the sound intense.

High intensity voicing poses a risk to vocal health

All high intensity voice production -- shouting, screaming, belting, operatic singing – has the potential to injure the voice. In Estill Voice Training, vocal health is paramount. This Figure is best learned and understood in context of shouting and/or belting, which in turn are best learned and understood once other Figures have been mastered. When this Figure is practiced in a Level One Course, limit practice to the silent preparation for a shout. It is recommended that this Figure be revisited during a Level Two Course.

Notes

The Two Conditions

Icon	Description	Schematic	Hand Signal
![vertical icon]	**Vertical** This is the condition during quiet breathing.		
![tilt icon]	**Tilt** This is the condition during shouting.		

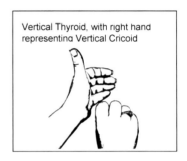

Vertical Thyroid, with right hand representing Vertical Cricoid

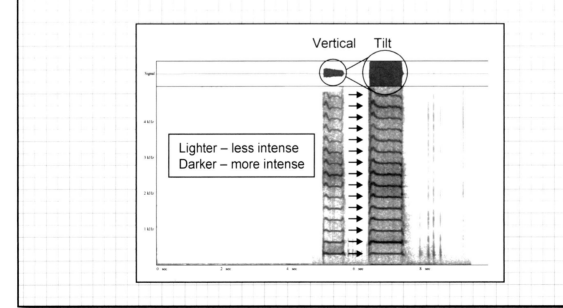

Estill Voiceprint Plus

When demonstrating or practicing this Figure with the *Estill Voiceprint Plus* program (Practice & Spectrogram Settings), look for the following visual cues in Tilt:

- Larger waveform
- Darker harmonics throughout the spectrum

Training Exercises

Vertical Cricoid

Relax the musculature surrounding the larynx and breathe quietly.
What do you feel in the C-T space?
This should be the Vertical Cricoid Cartilage condition.
Assign it a Number.

Cricoid Tilt

1) Make the preparation to shout as if at a sporting event and excited that the home team has just broken a tie and taken the lead. Start the preparation for a "Yeah!" But don't actually make the sound. Don't hold the breath, either. In fact, find the locus of Effort, assign it a number, and perform all of the Relaxation Maneuvers.

2) Make the preparation as above, Retract the FVFs, and actually shout / e / with a Glottal Onset or "yay!"
What do you feel?
If you feel a scratch at the true vocal folds, stop! Continue your practice of Cricoid Tilt in silence. You will learn how to apply Cricoid Tilt in the context of a safe Belt Quality in Level Two.

Notes

Figure for Cricoid Cartilage Control

On a vowel with Thick TVF: Body-Cover, demonstrate the following Cricoid Cartilage conditions:

1) Begin with Vertical Cricoid cartilage and change to Cricoid Tilt.
2) Begin with Cricoid Tilt and change to Vertical Cricoid.

Perform these tasks on / i, e, a, o, u /, at any pitch.
Practice moving between conditions abruptly, gradually.

Application

Cricoid Tilt is a defining attribute of the Belt voice quality and loud voicing.

Some of the concepts presented in this section of the course – most notably that more breath is *not* the only solution to making a more intense vocal sound – will help preserve vocal health.

LARYNX

Introductory Exercise

Place your hand over the larynx during this exercise.

Sustain / i / on a pitch in your speaking range.
  What do you feel? What do you hear?

Repeat the / i / at the same pitch, but this time pretending you are a very small, young child.
  What do you feel? What do you hear?
  What changed?

Repeat the / i / at the same pitch, but this time pretending you are a great opera singer.
  What do you feel? What do you hear?
  What changed?

> *Notes*

Anatomy & Physiology

The muscles responsible for larynx height were discussed in the Pitch section: the supra- and infra-hyoids. The activity of these muscles changes the length of the pharyngeal portion of the vocal tract.

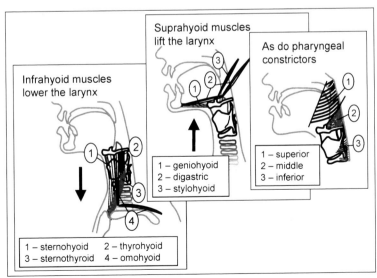

The Three Conditions

Icon	Condition & Description	Schematic	Hand Signal
	Low This is the condition of the larynx at low pitches, and in the preparation to sob.		
	Mid This position should correspond to the position of the larynx during quiet breathing		
	High This is the condition of the larynx at high pitches, and in the preparation to scream or squeal.		

Notes

Estill Voiceprint Plus

When demonstrating or practicing this Figure with the *Estill Voiceprint Plus* program look for the following visual cues:

- Movement of the formants in direct correlation with movement of the larynx — higher with a High Larynx, lower with a Low Larynx.

Enhance the visualization of formants by using the Resonance feature of *Estill Voiceprint Plus.* This setting will display the formants alone.

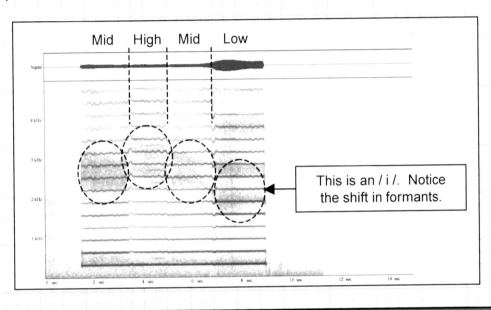

This is an / i /. Notice the shift in formants.

Training Exercises

Mid

1) Breathe quietly and feel for the position of the thyroid notch ("Adam's Apple") or cricoid arch in the neck. This should be the Mid condition.
2) Say or sing an / i / with Mid Larynx. What did you feel? What did you hear?
3) Say or sing the other vowels / i, e, a, o, u / with Mid Larynx. What did you feel? What did you hear?
4) From a comfortable mid-range pitch, sing up a one octave scale with a Mid Larynx.
   Repeat this exercise, singing down from the starting pitch.
   What did you feel? What did you hear?

Notes

High
1) Breathe quietly and feel for the position of the thyroid notch ("Adam's Apple") or cricoid arch in the neck, then silently prepare for a high pitch.
Or
Scream silently as we all might like to do from time to time, just to "let off steam."
Note the location of the sensation of Effort, give it a Number, hold it and carefully inhale and exhale. This should be a High Larynx condition.
2) Say or sing an / i / with High Larynx. What did you feel? What did you hear?
3) Say or sing the other vowels / e, a, o, u / with High Larynx. What did you feel? What did you hear?
4) From a high pitch, sing down a one octave scale with a High Larynx. What did you feel? What did you hear?

Low
1) Breathe quietly and feel for the position of the thyroid notch ("Adam's Apple") or cricoid arch in the neck, then silently prepare for a low pitch...
Or
Sob silently...
Or
Laugh silently, and very hard...
Note the location of the sensation of Effort, give it a Number, hold it and carefully inhale and exhale. This should be a Low Larynx condition.
2) Say or sing an / i / with Low Larynx. What did you feel? What did you hear?
3) Say or sing the other vowels / e, a, o, u / with Low Larynx. What did you feel? What did you hear?
4) From a low pitch, sing up a one octave scale with a Low Larynx. What did you feel? What did you hear?

Notes

Figure for Larynx Control

Demonstrate the following Larynx height conditions:

1) In a Mid Larynx position, speak normally.
2) On the same pitch, speak with a High Larynx.
3) On the same pitch, speak with a Low Larynx.
4) On a vowel, in sequence, Mid→High→Mid→Low→Mid.

Perform vowel task on / i, e, a, o, u /, at any pitch.
Practice moving between conditions abruptly, gradually.
Practice with different True Vocal Folds: Body-Cover conditions.

Application

Changing vocal tract length provides us with a variety of colors for speech and song.

- Low Larynx (long vocal tract) for a dark color and emotion
- High Larynx (short vocal tract) for a bright color and projection

Low Larynx is a feature of Operatic singing.

Mid Larynx is a feature of Speech quality.

High Larynx is a feature of Twang and Belting Qualities.

Velum

Introductory Exercise

Say, "hung" and prolong the / ŋ /.
Now, say "gee" and prolong the / i /.
Put them together, and say, "hung-gee hung-gee hung-gee"
  What do you feel?
  What do you hear?

Which condition had the greater sound energy, the "hung" or the "gee?"
Listen to someone *else* do this exercise.
  Which is louder?

Notes

Anatomy & Physiology

The position of the velum (soft palate) functions like a door to open or close the back entrances of both the oral cavity and the nose. Muscles that attach from above and below control the position of the velum. The doorway to the back of the nose is called the velopharyngeal port. The degree of opening or closing of the velopharyngeal port can be said to determine whether the sound from the larynx is resonated in the nose, the oral cavity, or both.

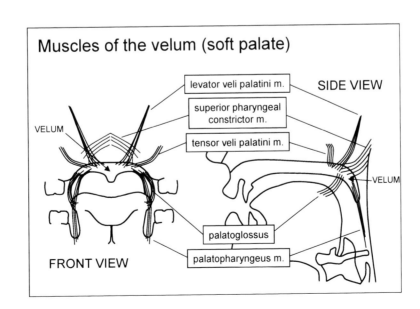

Muscles of the velum (soft palate)

The nasal passages act like acoustic baffles, filtering out high frequency energy. The nasal consonants / m /, / n /, and / ŋ / are resonated in the nasal passages only. In English, most vowels are resonated solely in the oral cavity. When a vowel is resonated in both the nose and oral cavity, it is nasalized. Nasalization (also called *nasalence*) is a linguistic feature of some languages, such as French. "Bon!" In English, vowels may be nasalized on the way to and from a nasal consonant.

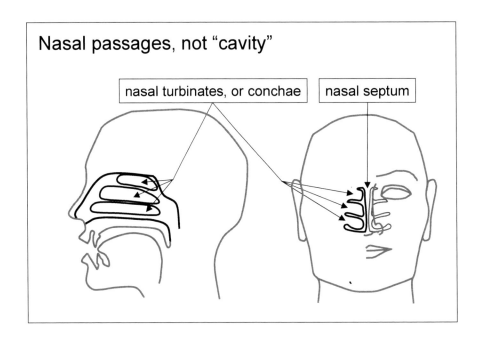

The Three Conditions

Icon	Condition & Description	Schematic	Hand Signal
	Low The velum is down, in contact with the back of the tongue. The velopharyngeal port is all the way open. The resonance is **nasal**.		
	Mid The velum is lifted away from the tongue, but not high enough to close the velopharyngeal port completely. The resonance is **nasalized**.		
	High The velum is up all the way, in contact with the walls of the nasopharynx. The velopharyngeal port is completely closed. The resonance is **oral**.		

Notes

Estill Voiceprint Plus

When practicing this Figure with the *Estill Voiceprint Plus* program (Practice & Spectrogram Settings), look for the following visual cues:

- Low – small waveform, very little high frequency energy at the top of the screen
- Mid – medium waveform, harmonics visible, but darker at low frequencies
- High – larger waveform, harmonics visible, with the most energy in the high frequency range

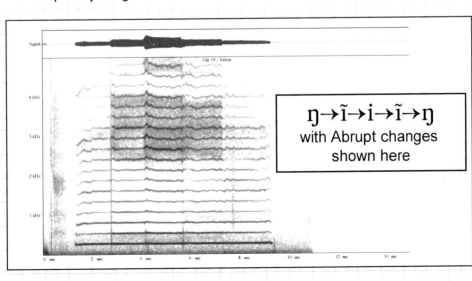

$\eta \rightarrow \tilde{\imath} \rightarrow i \rightarrow \tilde{\imath} \rightarrow \eta$
with Abrupt changes
shown here

Training Exercises

Increasing awareness of the Velum

1) Speak or sing "hu<u>ng</u>-gee" multiple times slowly, and with a strong / ŋ / and a strong / g /.

2) Repeat the exercise with other vowels, / e, a, o, u /.

    The Velum is moving between Low and High. Listen and feel for the change of resonance.

    Use the "nose test" (lightly and repeatedly pinch the nostrils closed). When the Velum is Low, in the / ŋ /, the tone should stop when pinching the nose. When the Velum is High, in the vowel following the / g /, there should be NO change during the nose test.

3) Repeat the exercise with each vowel, only this time make the repetitions as fast as possible. Work hard for vigorous movement of the velum and maintain rhythmically equal parts of the / ŋ / and the vowel.

    Singing this exercise on a higher pitch may make it easier.

    What do you feel?

    What do you hear?

Low

1) Speak or sing an / ŋ / and hold it. Feel the contact between velum and tongue.

    Use the "nose test" (lightly and repeatedly pinch the nostrils closed). Feel that the breath is escaping through the nose and not the mouth.

    The nose test result will be an on-off pulse of tone.

2) Practice Low Velum through the range.

Notes

Sing up/down one octave scales at various pitches, on the / ŋ /, with a Low Velum.

3) Practice Low Velum with different TVF: Body-Cover Conditions, using Slack, Thick, Thin, or Stiff.

Mid

1) Start with the / ŋ / and simply "break contact" between the tongue and the velum into the vowel which should become an / ĩ / (the *tilde* above the letter is the International Phonetic Alphabet diacritic marking for nasality). Or, simply say, "bon" (*en Français*).
Use the "nose test" (lightly and repeatedly pinch the nostrils closed). Feel that the breath is escaping through both the nose and the mouth.
Nose test results will be a fluctuation in tone, a pulsation of louder-softer.

2) Speak/sing other vowels with the Mid Velum: / i, e, a, o, u /. Nose test throughout to make sure resonance remains nasalized.

3) Count to ten with a half-open velar port. This will sound like the speech of a person with a neurological or structural defect preventing complete closure of the velopharyngeal port.

4) Practice Mid Velum through the range. Sing up/down one octave scales at various pitches, on different vowels, with a Mid Velum.

Notes

High

1) Speak or sing an / i /.
Feel the absence of contact between velum and tongue.
Use the "nose test" (lightly and repeatedly pinch your nostrils closed).
Feel that the breath is escaping through the mouth, not the nose.
Nose test results will be no change in tone.

2) Speak/sing other vowels with the High Velum: / i, e, a, o, u /.
Nose test throughout to make sure oral resonance is retained.

3) Practice High Velum across the range: Sing up/down one octave scales at various pitches, on different vowels, with a HighVelum.

Isolating Velum movement from tongue movement

1) Speak or sing the basic "hung-gee" repetition exercise, only this time, pay attention to the tongue and try to keep it out of the action. Drop the "hu" and simply say / ŋ / followed by the / g / and vowel.

2) Repeat the exercise with other vowels, / e, a, o, u /.

3) To better isolate the movement of the velum from the movement of the tongue, try the following:
   • "Pre-set" the tongue for each vowel, holding its position with tactile landmarks
   • Make the / g / softer, less athletic, less disruptive
   • Monitor by feeling the base of the tongue below the chin, or, use a mirror
   • Relax the tongue as much as the vowel will allow.

Notes

Figure for Velum Control

On a vowel, demonstrate the following Velum conditions:

1) Move the Velum from Low to High, abruptly, as in "hung-gee."
2) Alternate Low and High Velum as rapidly as possible.
3) Move the Velum from Low to High with no tongue movement.
4) Move the Velum from Low to High as slowly as possible and with no extraneous sounds.
5) Speak or sing with the Velum in its Mid position.
6) In sequence, Low →Mid →High →Mid →Low

Perform these tasks on / i, e, a, o, u /, at any pitch.
Practice moving between conditions abruptly, gradually.
Practice with different True Vocal Folds: Body-Cover conditions.

Notes

Application

There are times when we might *choose* to sing or speak with the Velum in any of its conditions:
- To hum...
- To produce an accent or characterization...
- To vary dynamics...

There are times when the Velum *unintentionally* shifts into its Mid position, "muting" the voice and prompting more work than would otherwise be needed to sustain a projected tone. This problem can be corrected by lifting the Velum to High, which will enhance high frequency resonance and projection.

Application Exercises: Mastering part 4 of the Figure (raising the Velum slowly and without extraneous sound), can add/subtract nasality to vary the intensity of the voice.

Sing up a scale in a comfortable range and gradually get softer and softer by *slowly* dropping the Velum from High to Low, opening the velopharyngeal port. Reverse the Velum's movement to grow louder while descending the scale, closing the velopharyngeal port.

Sing at a comfortable pitch with a High Velum and *decrescendo* (grow softer) by gradually dropping the Velum from High to Low. Reverse the process to *crescendo* (grow louder).

In many musical genres, singing high and soft is a much sought-after skill. One of the secrets to singing high and soft is to make sure the back of the tongue remains high, allowing the larynx the freedom to find the optimal position for each higher pitch. Remember to keep the larynx high (as in the Siren, producing high pitches is NOT about making more space). Isolated Velum Control can turn any pitch in the Siren into a soft tone.

To practice the very *small space* needed in the mouth to make any of the vowels at a high pitch, Siren the whole range on an / ŋ /. Make the Siren as soft as possible (review the Siren "recipe" as needed). Note how little open space there is between the tongue and roof of the mouth. Continue Sirening up and down and gradually raise the Velum into the vowel / u /, trying to keep very little open space in the mouth. Technically this will no longer be a Siren, but the sound should remain so soft that it sounds like the / ŋ /. Use the nose test to make sure that you are not nasalized.

Siren, gliding through the whole range, into other vowels in just the same way, / i, e, a, o, u /, changing only the Velum condition – from Low to High – keeping the intensity of each vowel as close to that of an / ŋ / as possible, and the space in the mouth small.

Siren up to some high pitch on an / ŋ /, and while sustaining that pitch, slowly "peel" the Low Velum from the tongue and up into its High condition. Use tongue bracing or the "y" glide device to avoid the noise associated with raising the Velum and closing the velopharyngeal port. While singing into a series of these high, soft vowels, perform the Relaxation Maneuvers.

TONGUE

Introductory Exercise

Say/sing / i – a – u /.
    What is moving?
Repeat without moving the lips.
    What do you hear?
    What is moving?
Repeat without moving the tongue.
    What do you hear?
    What is moving?
    Which exercise was easiest?

Allowing the tongue and lips to move as they usually would to form the vowels, sing a 2 octave scale, first on / i / and then on / a /.
    Was one scale easier to sing than the other?

Notes

Anatomy & Physiology

The musculature of the tongue is complex. Muscle fibers within the tongue run nearly every direction. The relaxed tongue expands to fill the oral cavity during quiet breathing through the nose.

Due to muscular complexity, activity in the tongue tip and blade can be isolated from activity in the dorsum and root. Vowel production influences pharyngeal dimension and tone quality. This is because the back of the tongue is the front of the throat. Many singers observe that / i / and / u / are easier to produce than / a /.

Muscles of the Tongue

Longitudinal
Transverse
Vertical
Genioglossus
Palatoglossus
Styloglossus
Hyoglossus

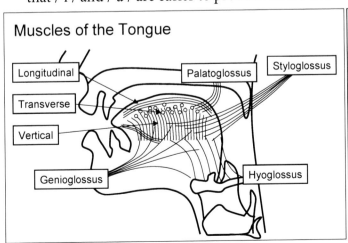

Parts of the Tongue

a. body
b. tip
c. blade
d. dorsum
e. root

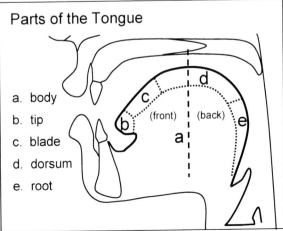

The acoustic characteristics of vowels are expressed as bandwidths of resonant intensity called *formants*. Numbered from low to high, the first 2 formants define a vowel. The formants appear like blocks of darkness on the *Estill Voiceprint Plus* spectrogram.

Notes

_____

_____

_____

_____

_____

The Four Conditions

Icon	Condition & Description	Schematic	Hand Signal
	Low This is the low, flat tongue dorsum taught in some voice studios where a dark tone is the goal.		
	Mid The tongue dorsum is in the position it usually occupies during speech, assuming that you speak without a strong regional accent or voice quality.		
	High The dorsum and root of the tongue are lifted, as they are in the vowel / i / or in the / j / ("y").		
	Compress An option used in dramatic operatic singing. The tongue tip is curled up and pulled back, while the back of the tongue is pushed forward, mounding and compressing the tongue.		

Notes

Estill Voiceprint Plus

When demonstrating or practicing this Figure with the *Estill Voiceprint Plus* program (Practice & Spectrogram Settings), look for the following visual cues:
- High – the formants will rise slightly, particularly the second
- Mid – the formants lie where they are during informal speech
- Low – the formants will fall slightly, particularly the second
- Compress – the formants will fall further

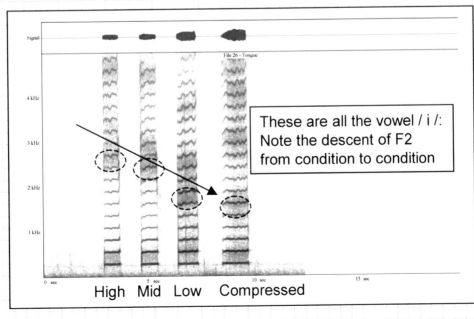

These are all the vowel / i /: Note the descent of F2 from condition to condition

Training Exercises

Isolating the tongue tip-and-blade from tongue dorsum-and-root.

1) Speak or sing a / ŋ / as in "si<u>ng</u>" as in the Low Velum task. Wiggle the tongue tip and blade to demonstrate independent movement of the tongue tip and blade.

2) Speak or sing a / ŋ / as above, and while humming, count from one to ten. This is mouthing the words, mirening. Exaggerate the movements of the front half of the tongue, the lips, the jaw, maintaining a stabile tongue dorsum, root and velum position.

Finding the tongue height attractor state

Count aloud from 1 to 10, slowly. Notice how the sides of the tongue in the region of the dorsum relte to the upper and lower molars.

Do the sides of the tongue hover near:

a) The upper molars (High)
b) Between upper and lower molars (Mid)
c) By the lower molars (Low)

One assumption is that the tongue is relaxed when in speech. It may not be. Another assumption is that speech would have a Mid tongue. It may not.

Mid

1) Say / a / as in an exclamation, "ah." The sides of the tongue at the dorsum should be *between* the upper and lower molars, as if about to be bitten. This is the Mid condition, and may feel like a "neutral" posture for the tongue.

Notes

2) Speak the alphabet with a Mid Tongue (to vary vowels, add consonants). How easy or difficult is it to speak clearly with this tongue condition?

3) Sing the alphabet song with a Mid Tongue (to vary pitch). What do you hear? What do you feel? Try it in a higher key, a lower key.

High

1) Say / i / or / ji / ("yee"). The tongue dorsum will lift, with the sides pressing on the inner surface of the upper molars – the *12 year molars*, not the wisdom teeth. This is High Tongue.

2) Recite the alphabet with a High Tongue (to vary vowels, add consonants). How easy or difficult is it to speak clearly with this tongue condition?

3) Sing the alphabet song with a High Tongue (to vary pitch). What do you hear? What do you feel? Try it in a higher key, a lower key.

Low

1) Say / a / as you might when a doctor is peering into your throat. Where do you feel the sides of your tongue? By the lower molars? If not, imagine a mouthful of "hot potatoes" and see if that brings the tongue into its Low condition.

2) Recite the alphabet with a Low Tongue (to vary vowels, add consonants). How easy or difficult is it to speak clearly with this tongue condition?

3) Sing the alphabet song with a Low Tongue (to vary pitch). What do you hear? What do you feel? Try it in a higher key, a lower key.

Notes

Tongue Height and Pitch

1) On a single pitch, speak or sing alternating between the / ŋ / as in "sing" and / ŋ / as in "song." Monitor the position of the hyoid bone. What do feel?

2) Hum through a 2 octave range on the / ŋ / of "sing" and repeat with the / ŋ / of "song."
   Which was easier, the "sing" or the "song?"

Compress

1) With the forefinger on the underside of the curled up tip of the tongue, press the tongue tip as far back as possible (without choking, of course), then press the back of the tongue forward against the finger, as hard as possible. The dorsum will be high. Holding these Effort Numbers in the tongue, remove the finger and hold the Compressed Tongue.

2) Say or sing an / i / with Thin TVF: Body-Cover and Mid Tongue. In midst of this / i /, Compress the Tongue.
   What do you feel?
   What do you hear?

3) Say the alphabet with Compressed Tongue (to vary vowels).
   What do you feel?
   What do you hear?

4) Sing the alphabet song with Compressed Tongue (to vary pitches).
   What do you hear? What do you feel? Try it in a higher key, a lower key.

Notes

Figure for Tongue Control

Demonstrate the following Tongue conditions:

1) Pitch glide on / ŋ / with High Tongue. Repeat with Low Tongue.
2) Speak clearly with Mid Tongue. Repeat with High Tongue.
3) On a vowel, alternate between Mid and Compressed Tongue.
4) In sequence, / i→ e→ a→ o→ u / with High Tongue, to demonstrate equal brightness.
5) With a High Tongue / ŋ /, "Miren" a song demonstrating independent movement of tongue tip, blade, and jaw.
6) On a vowel, in sequence, Mid→Low→Mid→High→Compress.

Perform vowel tasks on / i, e, a, o, u /, at any pitch.
Practice moving between conditions abruptly, gradually.
Practice with different True Vocal Folds: Body-Cover conditions.

Application

This Figure increases awareness of the several parts of the tongue that can be independently controlled.

Because the tongue forms the front wall of the throat, tongue position is crucial to voice quality control – if there is too much of a change in position between front and back vowels, voice quality can be compromised. A High Tongue can hlep to equalize resonance.

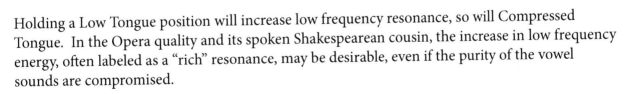

As activity in the tongue root can influence the vertical mobility of the larynx, care must be taken in any singing voice quality to ensure that tongue position does not compromise pitch.

Holding a Low Tongue position will increase low frequency resonance, so will Compressed Tongue. In the Opera quality and its spoken Shakespearean cousin, the increase in low frequency energy, often labeled as a "rich" resonance, may be desirable, even if the purity of the vowel sounds are compromised.

In qualities where a high laryngeal position is required, such as Twang and Belting, the High option is the Tongue position of choice. FVF Retraction is essential in these qualities.

Application Exercise: Try the Pitch Exercise once again. This time, see if a High Tongue helps extend the range (remember to Retract the FVFs).

ARYEPIGLOTTIC SPHINCTER

Introductory Exercise

Say/sing **"nyae,** ₙyₐₑ, **nyae,** nyae, ₙyₐₑ**!"**
(The schoolyard sing-song taunt)
    What do you hear?
    What do you feel?
Is the tone bright and piercing?
To make this sound brighter yet, use
High Tongue.
Did you feel FVF constriction?
If you did, use a Mid Velum, and Retract
the FVFs.

Notes

Anatomy & Physiology

Narrowing of the epilarynx (the tube above the true vocal folds formed by the aryepiglottic sphincter or AES) creates a formant between 2-4 kHz (2000 – 4000 Hz). The bright and piercing change in voice quality associated with AES narrowing is the primary feature of the voice quality called "Twang" in Estill Voice Training®.

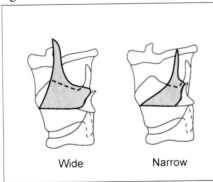

Wide   Narrow

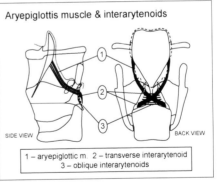

Aryepiglottis muscle & interarytenoids

SIDE VIEW   BACK VIEW

1 – aryepiglottic m. 2 – transverse interarytenoid
3 – oblique interarytenoids

AES Narrowing makes the voice loud

The bandwidth of the AES Narrowing corresponds to the resonant frequency of the ear canal. This means that sounds matching this frequency will resonate in the ear canals of a listener, making them *louder*. Loudness is a perception, not an absolute, and does not correspond to intensity directly. Loudness is heavily influenced by pitch/frequency.

There may be breath and true vocal fold side-effects when the epilarynx is narrowed as well. It is hypothesized that with this narrowing, the vocal folds stay closed a little longer, as they might were they thicker. A longer closed phase means higher subglottal air pressure, a more intense sound source.

False Vocal Fold Constriction is a risk with AES Narrowing and Twang

Constrictive closure of the true vocal folds, false vocal folds, and velopharygeal port all occur in swallowing. Aryepiglottic narrowing is part of that swallowing sequence. Because of this, AES Narrowing during phonation may trigger other swallowing muscle activity in the larynx, i.e. FVF Constriction.

Problem: "Closure" is desired at both the lowest and highest levels of the larynx without engaging FVF Constriction in the middle.

Solution: "Block" the physiological muscle patterns of swallowing by leaving the velopharyngeal port open and learn to Twang with a Mid Velum.

Confusion is a risk with Twang

The piercingly bright tone produced with AES Narrowing is often misunderstood and described as a "nasal" sound. Remember that nasal resonance favors low frequencies. The high frequency formant of Twang is produced in the epilaryngeal space. For reasons explained above it may be nasalized, which might actually dull the tone slightly.

Notes

The Two Conditions

Icon	Condition & Description	Schematic	Hand Signal
	Wide — This is the option where Twang is turned off, and the AES is Wide.		
	Narrow — This is the option we have been experiencing in the "nyae-nyae's".		

Notes

Estill Voiceprint Plus

When demonstrating or practicing this Figure with the *Estill Voiceprint Plus* program (Practice & Spectrogram Settings), look for the following visual cues:

- Narrow– the bright formant band somewhere between 2000 and 4000 Hz, across all vowels.
- Wide – the drop in energy in the 2000 to 4000 Hz region

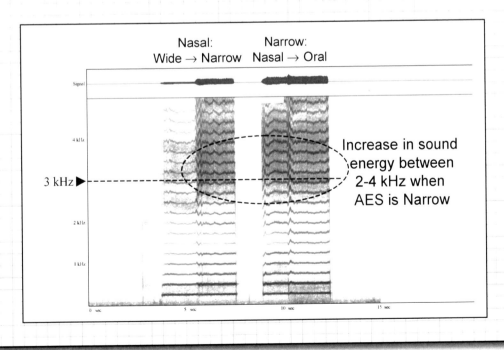

Training Exercises

Narrow, without FVF Constriction

1) Demonstrate nasality with a Thin TVF: Body-Cover on all vowels.
   Use the nose test to verify that the Velum is in its Mid condition, with breath escaping through both the mouth and the nose.
2) Start with a nasalized / i /, as above, and Narrow the AES.
3) Start with other vowels, / e, a, o, u /, and Narrow the AES.
4) Sing up and down octave scales with a Narrow AES.

Problem: Vowels are not equally bright.
Solution:
1) Find the pitch and vowel where Twang is the brightest.
2) While moving from this "best" vowel into each of the others, move the tongue dorsum forward/back, higher/lower, until each vowel matches the best one.

Problem: Pitches are not equally bright.
Solution:
1) Find the pitch and vowel where the nasalized Twang is brightest.
2) Ascend or descend a scale from that pitch, on that vowel, matching each note in brightness with the first (best, Twangiest) tone. Sing back and forth from the starting pitch through all the scale steps.

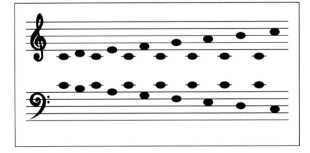

Notes

Wide

1) Speak or sing an / a / with a Wide AES.
2) Speak or sing other vowels with a Wide AES, / i, e, o, u /.
3) Sing up and down octave scales with a Wide AES.
   Sing scales on different vowels.

Isolating Velum condition from the Narrowed AES

Narrow the AES and move between the 3 conditions of the Velum:
Low – Mid – High – Mid – Low.

This is not an easy task, but it demonstrates that the presence/absence of Twang is independent of the presence/absence of nasality.

Notes

Figure for Aryepiglottic Sphincter Control

Demonstrate the following AES conditions:

1) On a vowel with Thin TVF: Body-Cover and Mid Velum (nasalized), a Wide AES.
2) On a nasalized Thin fold vowel, change from Wide to Narrow AES.
3) On a nasalized Thin fold vowel with Narrow AES, an octave scale with equal brightness between pitches.
4) In nasalized Thin folds with Narrow AES, the sequence / i→e→a→o→u / demonstrating equal brightness between vowels.
5) From a nasalized Thin fold vowel with Narrow AES, demonstrate a change from Mid to High Velum.

Perform vowel tasks on / i, e, a, o, u /, at any pitch.
Practice moving between conditions abruptly, gradually.
Practice with different True Vocal Fold: Body-Cover conditions.

Application

Narrowing the AES provides loudness without any increase of Effort at the level of the vocal folds. It is an essential component of singing in Opera and Belt qualities, but is also heard in "character" voices, spoken and sung.
A Narrow AES can also be used to monitor for tongue control, and to equalize vowels and identify aspects of consonant production that compromise consistent voice quality.

Application Exercise: Sing "Happy Birthday" again, with a Narrow AES. Match the resonant brightness from vowel to vowel. Some vowels, some pitches, will be easier than others. Using a High Tongue and FVF Retraction will help.

Jaw

Introductory Exercise

Sing "Happy Birthday" with the teeth barely separated – and do not open the mouth further.

Sing this song again, with the mouth wide open.

What do you feel?
What do you hear?

Notes

Anatomy & Physiology

The role of serendipity

When Jo Estill tried the "steel tongue maneuver" (an exercise she devised for High Tongue) and inadvertently raised her Velum, the sound that resulted was exceedingly "dark."

The "Steel Tongue Maneuver"

a) Make an / ŋ / as in / ɪŋ /, keeping the sides of the tongue pressed against the back molars.

b) Simultaneously make an / n / with the tip of the tongue against the alveolar ridge (just behind the front teeth).

c) Now, gradually pull the tip of the tongue and the / n / back along the roof of the mouth to meet the / ŋ /. Feel like a "steel tongue" to you?

d) Hold all these "steel tongue" Effort numbers, raise the Velum and sing / i, e, a, o, u /. If you have produced this maneuver correctly, you will have a curiously "dark" resonance.

The role of research

In videoendoscopic observation of the "Steel Tongue Maneuver," it was noted that there was a *huge* width of space in the vocal tract at the level of the back of the tongue. It was thought that the forward movement of the tongue base made a wider tube, darker resonance.

Exercise:

Repeat the "Steel Tongue Maneuver," keeping a finger on the chin. As the / n / (tongue tip) is pulled back," there may be a subtle backwards movement of the jaw.

Parallel research with X-rays, revealed that it was jaw movement, not tongue movement. When the maneuver was performed without the jaw moving back, the sound was "brilliant," not "dark." Research leads to more questions, for which there are currently no answers.

The role of anatomy

Given the relationship of the muscles and ligaments that attach to the mandible (jaw bone) and the pharyngeal constrictors, the influence of jaw position on pharyngeal width is understandable.

The jaw joint, the temporomandibular joint (TMJ), normally moves freely in several directions, allowing the jaw to glide forward, glide forward and drop down open, to remain in its rest position swinging down and open, and to move sidewise as in the grinding action of chewing.

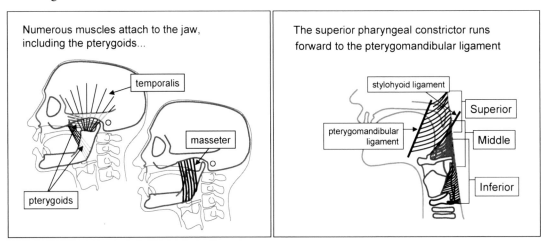

Numerous muscles attach to the jaw, including the pterygoids...
temporalis
masseter
pterygoids

The superior pharyngeal constrictor runs forward to the pterygomandibular ligament
stylohyoid ligament
pterygomandibular ligament
Superior
Middle
Inferior

Notes

Please Note: The following exercises presume a healthy jaw joint. If "TMJ" problems (Temporo-Mandibular Joint Dysfunction) exist, monitor very carefully in the following exercises. Use very small Effort Numbers initially, and avoid those conditions that cause pain or immobilize the joint.

The Four Conditions

Icon	Description	Schematic
	Forward In this condition, the chin is jutted forward, putting lower teeth and jaw ahead of the upper teeth.	
	Mid This is the alignment of a normal bite, with jaw slightly dropped.	
	Back The lower teeth are pulled back behind the upper teeth, pronounced "over-bite."	
	Drop This is the extreme "drop" of the jaw.	

Notes

_____

_____

_____

_____

_____

_____

Estill Voiceprint Plus

When demonstrating or practicing this Figure with the *Estill Voiceprint Plus* program (Practice & Resonance Settings), look for the following visual cues:
- Formant shifting – upwards for Mid, downward for Forward, Back and Dropped

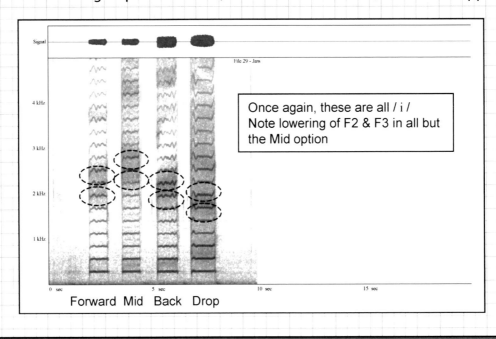

Once again, these are all / i /
Note lowering of F2 & F3 in all but the Mid option

Forward   Mid   Back   Drop

Training Exercises

Mid

1) Perform the first few parts of the Relaxation Maneuver to arrive at a Mid Jaw condition. The jaw should "release" into this condition, opening slightly, with the upper incisors (front teeth) just forward of the lower.

2) Speak or sing an / i / with Mid Jaw on a comfortable pitch.

3) Speak or sing these other vowels with Mid Jaw: / e, a, o, u /.

4) Sing / i-e-a-o-u / (a slow motion "(m) eow") with Mid Jaw on every scale step through a 2 octave range. Use Thin TVF: Body-Cover and Retracted FVFs, singing softly.
What do you feel?
What do you hear?

Notes

Forward

1) Position the jaw so that the lower incisors are ahead of the uppers, Forward Jaw.
2) Speak or sing an / i / with Forward Jaw on a comfortable pitch.
3) Speak or sing these other vowels with Forward Jaw: / i, e, a, o, u /.
4) Sing / i-e-a-o-u / (a slow motion "(m) eow") with Forward Jaw on every scale step through a 2 octave range. Use Thin TVF: Body-Cover and Retracted FVFs, singing softly.
   What do you feel?
   What do you hear?

Back

1) Pull the jaw straight back. Locate the Effort of the Jaw Back condition and then proceed through the Relaxation Maneuvers to isolate this Effort from the tongue.
2) Speak or sing an / i / with Back Jaw on a comfortable pitch.
3) Speak or sing these other vowels with Back Jaw: / e, a, o, u /.
4) Sing / i-e-a-o-u / (a slow motion "(m) eow") with Back Jaw on every scale step through a 2 octave range. Use Thin TVF: Body-Cover and Retracted FVFs, singing softly.
   What do you feel?
   What do you hear?

Drop

1) Drop the Jaw as far as possible. Note that the jaw can be dropped in two ways: from the Mid condition, or, from the Forward condition. The Protruded option will allow greater Drop.
2) Speak or sing an / i / with Dropped Jaw on a comfortable pitch.

Notes

3) Speak or sing these other vowels with Dropped Jaw: / e, a, o, u /.

4) Sing / i-e-a-o-u / (a slow motion "(m) eow") with Dropped Jaw on every scale step through a 2 octave range. Use Thin TVF: Body-Cover and Retracted FVFs, singing softly.
What do you feel?
What do you hear?

Notes

_____

_____

_____

_____

_____

_____

_____

_____

_____

Figure for Jaw Control

Demonstrate the following Jaw conditions:

1) With Mid Jaw, speak normally.
2) On the same pitch, speak with a Forward Jaw.
3) On the same pitch, speak with a Back Jaw.
4) On the same pitch, speak with a Dropped Jaw.
5) On a vowel, in sequence, Mid→Forward→Mid→Back→Mid, using High Tongue for consistent control of that structure.
6) On a vowel, in sequence, Mid→Drop→Mid, using High Tongue for consistent control of that structure.

Perform the vowel task on / i, e, a, o, u /, at any pitch.
Practice moving between conditions abruptly, gradually.
Practice with different True Vocal Folds: Body-Cover conditions.

Application

Both actors and singers manipulate jaw position to influence the sound of the voice.
These choices may seem puzzling. For example, why does one singer sing with very "natural" Mid Jaw position, and another with an exaggerated Drop, or Back position?
The answers may lie in the pharynx and the acoustic effect of that choice on voice quality.

LIPS

Introductory Exercise

Say, sing, or shout, "**Hooo-eeee!**"
   What do you feel in the lips?

Sing a simple song with exaggerated lip rounding, as in the "Hooo."
Sing the same song with exaggerated pulling back on the corners of the mouth, as in an exaggerated "eeee!"

   What do you feel?
   What do you hear?

Notes

_____

_____

_____

_____

_____

_____

Anatomy & Physiology

The primary muscle of the lips is the orbicularis oris. It encircles the mouth. It is a sphincter, as is apparent in puckering the lips. A number of muscles come in to the orbicularis oris from different angles to pull the lips up, down, and out from different angles. The muscles that spread the lips are the risorius (pulls straight back) and zygomaticus muscles, major and minor (pull up and back).

Lip posture affects vocal tract length

With Lip Protrusion, the overall length of the vocal tract is increased. With Lip Spreading, the length of the vocal tract is shortened. The condition that makes the vocal tract tubing longer favors bass resonance; the condition that shortens the tube favors treble.

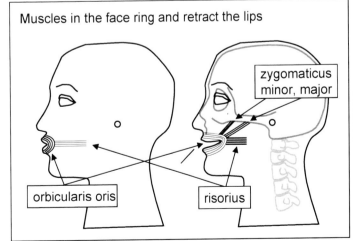

Muscles in the face ring and retract the lips

zygomaticus minor, major

orbicularis oris

risorius

The Three Conditions

Icon	Condition & Description	Schematic
	Protrude The lips extend forward of the face in this condition.	
	Mid The lips are as they typically are in normal speech, "neutral," or "relaxed."	
	Spread This is the condition of the broadest possible smile.	

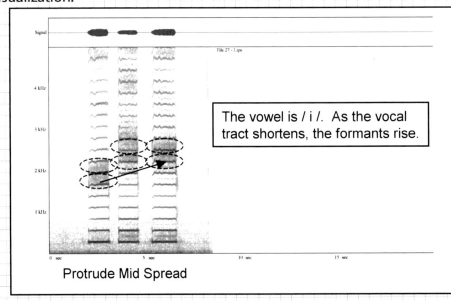

Estill Voiceprint Plus

When demonstrating or practicing this Figure with the *Estill Voiceprint Plus* program, look for the following visual cues:

- Movement of the formants up with Spreading and down with Protruding

Using the resonance feature of *Estill Voiceprint Plus* can enhance formant visualization.

> The vowel is / i /. As the vocal tract shortens, the formants rise.

Protrude Mid Spread

Training Exercises

Mid

1) Massage the lips to establish a Mid Lips condition.
2) Speak or sing an / i / with Mid Lips on a comfortable pitch.
3) Speak these other vowels with Mid Lips: / e, a, o, u /. Note that there will be some lip-rounding on the / o / and / u /.
4) Sing / i-e-a-o-u / (a slow motion "(m) eow") with Mid Lips on every scale step through a 2 octave range. Use Thin TVF: Body-Cover and Retracted FVFs, singing softly. The range of movement of your lips should remain the same as the spoken example.
   What do you feel?
   What do you hear?

Protrude

1) Pucker the lips somewhat, and Protrude them forward as far as possible. Locate the Effort, assign it a Number, and hold.
2) Speak or sing an / i / with Protruded Lips on a comfortable pitch.
3) Speak these other vowels with Protruded Lips: / e, a, o, u /.
4) Sing / i-e-a-o-u / (a slow motion "(m) eow") with Protruded Lips on every scale step through a 2 octave range. Use Thin TVF: Body-Cover and Retracted FVFs, singing softly.
   What do you feel?
   What do you hear?

Notes

Spread

1) Smile as widely as possible. Locate the Effort, assign it a Number, and hold.
2) Speak or sing an / i / with Spread Lips on a comfortable pitch.
3) Speak these other vowels with Spread Lips: / e, a, o, u /.
4) Sing / i-e-a-o-u / (a slow motion "(m) eow") with Spread Lips on every scale step through a 2 octave range. Use Thin TVF: Body-Cover and Retracted FVFs, singing softly. The range of movement of the lips should remain the same as the spoken example, which is to say that there will be some accommodation for lip-rounding on the / o / and / u /.

Notes

Figure for Lip Control

Demonstrate the following Lip conditions:

1) With Mid Lips, speak normally.
2) On the same pitch, speak with a Protruded Lips.
3) On the same pitch, speak with a Spread Lips.
4) On a vowel, in sequence, Mid→Protrude→Mid→Spread→Mid, using High Tongue for consistent control of that structure.

Perform the vowel task on / i, e, a, o, u /, at any pitch.
Practice moving between conditions abruptly, gradually.
Practice with different True Vocal Folds: Body-Cover conditions.

Application

There are differences in vocal color with different lip conditions. The effects of Lip Control are subtle.

Protruding the lips instantly makes the sound a little darker. Some choral conductors and some operatic singers use this option *all* the time.

Conversely, these same conductors and singers would tend to avoid the opposite lip condition with the corners of the mouth pulled back. Indeed, the brightness of tone associated with this effectively shortened oral cavity is often called "spread" in a pejorative sense. "Bright" is a choice and welcomed in some spoken character voices and singing voice qualities.

In this video age, one can find singers in almost every genre choosing to use Protruded Lips to "darken" a tone, Spread Lips for a "brighter" sound.

Application Exercise: Sing "Happy Birthday" line by line with Protruded, Mid, and then Spread Lips. What do you hear?

HEAD AND NECK

Introductory Exercise

Take a pen (or pencil) and a piece of paper and prepare to sign your name, *only* do NOT let your hand rest on the writing surface. Go ahead and sign your name with only the pen in contact with the paper.

Sign your name again with your hand resting on the writing surface.

Which was easier, and why?

Notes

Anatomy & Physiology

When the skeletal structures of the Head & Neck are Anchored, or "braced," the smaller muscles that control the vocal folds can fine-tune their adjustments within a stable external framework. The result is that these smaller muscles do not have to work so hard.

Please Note: As with good vocal health (see page vii), good postural alignment with no history of neck or back problems is assumed. Please inform your instructor if back or neck injuries exist and refrain from practice of this Figure.

X-Rays of Head & Neck Anchoring

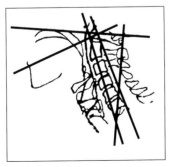

At Rest

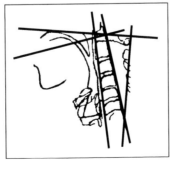
Anchored

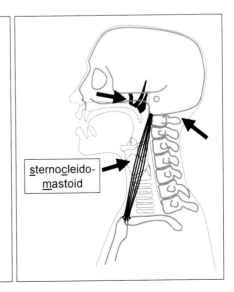

sternocleido-mastoid

The Two Conditions

Icon	Condition Description	Schematic	Hand Signal
R	**Relax** This is postural "resting" or neutral state.		
A	**Anchor** In this condition, muscles above the soft palate, to the sides of the neck, and in the occipital region are engaged.		

Notes

_____

_____

_____

_____

_____

_____

_____

_____

_____

_____

_____

_____

_____

_____

_____

_____

Estill Voiceprint Plus

When demonstrating or practicing this Figure with the *Estill Voiceprint Plus* program
(Practice & Spectrogram Settings), look for the following visual cue:
• Increased energy in all the harmonic traces with Anchored condition
Note that if the vowel formants drop during Anchoring, the tongue and/or larynx may
be lowering. To avoid this, brace the tongue on the molars and monitor the position
of the cricoid cartilage in the neck.

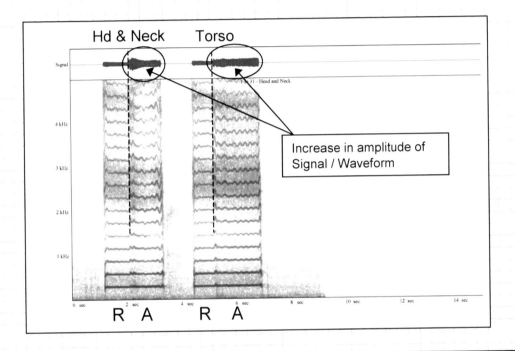

Training Exercises

Exercises to trigger Effort for Head & Neck Anchoring

1) Sit-ups
   Lie on the floor and *start* do a sit-up –
   do not even lift the head off the floor.
   What do you feel?
   This is a natural way to contract the
   sternocleidomastoids (SCMs).
   Practice a "sit-up" while standing.

2) Nostril Flare
   With the vocal folds open (breathing
   easily), dilate the nostrils as far as
   possible. Try to reach to the ears with
   the nostrils. Do not use your lips.
   Where do you feel Effort?

3) The Apple Bite
   Pretend to sink the upper teeth into a
   hard juicy apple that is covered with
   sticky caramel. The teeth sink in
   without biting all the way through, and
   become stuck in the caramel. Try to
   pull the teeth out, without moving the
   lower jaw.
   Where do you feel Effort?

Feel for the Effort in four places:

- Behind the upper front teeth under the
  nose
- Back to the velum, and up into the
  center of the head
- Under the ear, to the occipital bone at
  the nape of the neck
- A sensation of two struts, or columns,
  to either side of the neck

Yet another "trigger" for Head & Neck Anchoring, with voicing

1) Take a straw and try to suck through
   it while blocking the far end with one
   finger.
   Or... Suck on the end of the thumb.
   Feel for Effort locations, as listed above.

Notes

2) "Wean" from the straw or the thumb by placing the thumb-tip lightly on the lips while sucking in. Continue holding this sucking-pulling condition, and simultaneously sing a / ŋ /, softly. Sing a melody on / ŋ /. Notice the sensation of pulling "in" and singing "out" at the same time.
Perform the Relaxation Maneuvers while singing.

3) Repeat the song above, and while singing, lift the Velum to High, continuing the melody on an / i /. Avoid singing more loudly once the velopharyngeal port has been closed. **Note:** Head & Neck Anchoring is used for more power in the speaking or singing voice, but it also adds "intensity" to soft voicing.

Alternating Relaxed and Anchored

1) Perform the first few Relaxation Maneuvers to establish the Relaxed Head & Neck Condition.

2) Practice seeing how quickly Head and Neck Anchoring can be assumed. That is, practice establishing Effort numbers in the roof of the mouth, above the velum/in the center of the head, in the nape of the neck, and to the sides of the neck.

3) Practice while walking: 4 steps Anchored, 4 steps Relaxed.

4) Increase the time Anchored, without losing the Number.

5) Practice changing from Relaxed to Anchored, with tone, as in the Figure .

6) Match or exceed the Anchoring Number with Effort in Retraction of the FVFs.

Notes

Figure for Head & Neck Control

Demonstrate the following Head & Neck conditions:
1)   Speak or sing with Thin TVF: Body-Cover on / i /, add FVF Retraction |←→|
and then *suddenly* Anchor the Head & Neck.
2)   Speak or sing with Thin TVF: Body-Cover on / i /, add FVF Retraction |←→|
and then *gradually* Anchor the Head & Neck.

Perform on / i, e, a, o, u /, at any pitch.
Practice with different Effort Numbers.
Practice with different True Vocal Folds: Body-Cover conditions.
Practice allowing for the inadvertent increase in sound intensity with Anchoring.
Practice equalizing the intensity between Head & Neck conditions.
Practice independently of and in combination with Torso Anchoring.

Application

Head & Neck Anchoring provides greater stability and consistency in voice performance.

When in a part of the range where the voice might want to involuntarily shift gears, try Head & Neck Anchoring. This applies equally when trying to remain in a given voice quality outside of the pitch or dynamic range it naturally favors.

If power or projection is needed, then Head & Neck Anchoring is one option that delivers an increase in intensity while keeping a MCVE at the level of the true vocal folds.

Head & Neck Anchoring is obligatory in the high intensity voice qualities of Opera and Belt.

As in the pen and paper exercise, Head & Neck Control uses big muscles so the little muscles do not have to work so hard!

Torso

Introductory Exercise

Sing or speak part of a song or speech you would like to perform more powerfully in a very casual, relaxed posture.

Assume the posture of an operatic singer, or the strong stance of Superman, and sing or speak again.

What is happening in the larynx?
What is happening to the breath?

Notes

_____

_____

_____

_____

_____

Please Note: As with good vocal health (see page vii), good postural alignment with no history of neck or back problems is assumed. If back or neck problems are present, please inform the instructor and refrain from practice of this Figure.

Anatomy & Physiology

The muscle activity we cultivate in Torso Anchoring includes the muscles identified below. There are other muscles in the back that get recruited as well.

This activity tends to spread the rib cage and lift the sternum slightly. If the torso feels compressed during practice of the Torso Anchor, the Figure is being performed incorrectly.

This muscle activity appears to stabilize the spine and rib cage. It should not interfere with breathing: respiratory stuctures and musculature should remain free to move. The experience is of the breath being supported. Muscle Effort sometimes spreads in fortuitous ways. This is described as a flow-on effect, and Torso Anchoring is an example of this phenomenon.

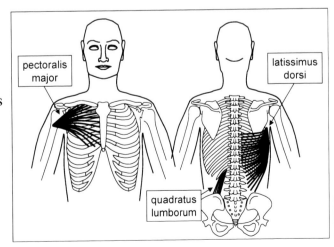

pectoralis major

latissimus dorsi

quadratus lumborum

The Two Conditions

Icon	Condition & Description	Schematic	Hand Signal
R	**Relax** This is the condition assumed when sitting or standing in a comfortably upright posture: not slumping, and not straining to straighten up.		
A	**Anchor** When the Torso Anchor is engaged, the "pecs" and "lats" are contracted. The shoulders may pull down slightly; the sternum may lift.		

Estill Voiceprint Plus

When demonstrating or practicing this Figure with the *Estill Voiceprint Plus* program (Practice & Spectrogram Settings), look for the following visual cues:

- In the Anchored condition, watch for an increase in the size of the waveform and increased brightness in all harmonics

As with Head & Neck Anchoring, watch for formant shifts that might reveal a change in tongue or larynx height.

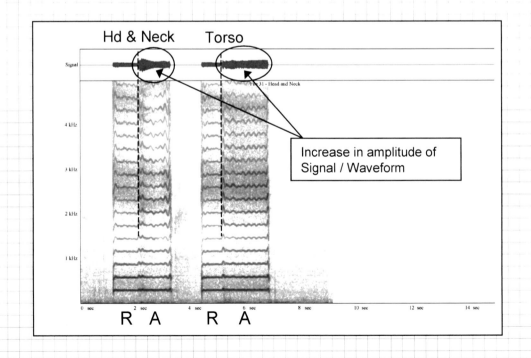

112

Notes

_____
_____
_____
_____
_____
_____

Training Exercises

Finding the Effort Locations for Torso Anchoring

1) Pretend to have an under inflated balloon in each armpit. Squeeze the balloons with your arms. Do not close the distance between the shoulder blades while squeezing.
What do you feel?
Hold the Number and breathe.

2) Pretend to pull on imaginary rings at the ends of elastic strips:
   - Hanging from the ceiling
   - Attached to the walls to either side
   - Attached to the wall ahead
   - Attached to the floor at either sides
   Once again, do not close the distance between the shoulder blades.
   What do you feel?
   Hold the Number and breathe.

3) Exhale and pull the shoulders down, hard. Not forward, nor backward.
   Down.
   Locate and quantify the Effort.
   Hold the Number and breathe.
   Perform the Relaxation Maneuvers.

Notes

_____
_____
_____
_____
_____
_____
_____
_____
_____
_____
_____

Feel for the Effort in four places:

- Below the shoulder blades in the contraction of the latissimus dorsi muscles
- In the outward expansion of the back just below the arm pits
- In the tug of the quadratus lumborum in the small of the back
- In the lift of the sternum and pull of the pectoralis muscles across the chest

Note: This activity does not interfere with breathing at all. Anchor the Torso and perform the Relaxation Maneuvers, Anchoring while breathing in and out, walking briskly, etc..

Alternating Relaxed and Anchored conditions

1) Gently stretch and move around to establish the Relaxed Torso Condition.
2) Practice seeing how fast the condition of Torso Anchoring can be assumed.
3) Practice Retraction of the FVFs with the Torso Anchoring.
4) Practice while walking briskly, so many steps Anchored, then so many steps Relaxed. Remember that walking briskly releases the muscles involved in breathing.
5) Practice using different Numbers each time the Torso Anchor is engaged.
6) Increase the time holding the Anchored condition.

Practice of Head & Neck and Torso Anchoring together, separately

1) Practice seeing how fast both Head and Neck and Torso Anchoring can be assumed.
2) While walking briskly, alternate between Anchoring the Head and Neck and Anchoring the Torso, then Anchor both simultaneously.
3) Remember to keep the False Vocal

Notes

Folds Retracted throughout! This adds another dimension of Effort, but it will be needed when adding the voice

Practicing Anchoring in silence

1) "Speak/sing" several phrases from a speech/song *in silence*, with a Relaxed Torso condition. Pretend to actually be speaking/singing, inhaling and exhaling as normal.
What do you feel?

2) "Speak/sing" the same several phrases from this speech/song *in silence*, with an Anchored Torso condition.
What do you feel?

3) Repeat the exercise in the step above, only this time Retract the FVFs throughout the phrases, *and* the inhalations that follow. Match or exceed the Anchoring Number with Effort in Retraction of the FVFs
What do you feel?

4) Repeat this exercise with Torso Anchoring and FVF Retraction, only this time gradually increase the Numbers on both Anchoring and Retraction when approaching the end of every phrase.
What do you feel?

Practicing Anchoring in speech or song

1) Speak/sing (out loud) several phrases from the speech/song used in the exercise above, with a Relaxed Torso condition.
What do you feel?

2) Speak/sing the same several phrases from this speech/song, with an Anchored Torso condition.
What do you feel?

Notes

3) Repeat the exercise in the step above, only this time Retract the FVFs throughout the phrases, *and* the inhalations that follow. Match or exceed the Anchoring Number with Effort in Retraction of the FVFs. What do you feel?

4) Repeat this exercise with Torso Anchoring and FVF Retraction, only this time gradually increase the Numbers on both Anchoring and Retraction when approaching the end of every phrase.
What do you feel?

Notes

Figure for Torso Control

Demonstrate the following Torso conditions:
1) Speak or sing with Thin TVF: Body-Cover on / i /, add FVF Retraction |←→|, and then *suddenly* Anchor the Torso.
2) Speak or sing with Thin TVF: Body-Cover on / i /, add FVF Retraction |←→|, and then *gradually* Anchor the Torso.

Perform on / i, e, a, o, u /, at any pitch.
Practice with different Effort Numbers.
Practice with different True Vocal Folds: Body-Cover conditions.
Practice allowing for the inadvertent increase in sound intensity with Anchoring.
Practice equalizing the intensity between Torso conditions.
Practice independently from and in combination with Head & Neck Anchoring.

Application

The contribution of Anchoring to singing and speaking is simple: it allows singing and speaking with increased power *and* MCVE (most comfortable vocal effort) at the level of the true vocal folds.

Anchoring is singing with **SUPPORT**.

Anchoring is an option to increase the intensity of any voice quality; it is obligatory with the high intensity voice qualities, Opera and Belt.

As with Head & Neck Anchoring, Torso Anchoring can also add emotional intensity and/or stability to a soft tone.

WHAT'S NEXT?

Many students of this work have stunning insights during their first encounter. Sometimes a persistent vocal problem is instantly solved through a more-informed awareness of how the voice works. Paradoxically, although Figures for Voice™ can fix problems quickly, Estill Voice Training® is decidedly not a "quick fix." Estill Mentor and Course Instructors and Estill Master Trainers can demonstrate impressive feats of vocal control. What is not immediately apparent is the time invested in study and practice to make this possible.

The exercises in this *Workbook* have been basic and introductory. The time lines for the acquisition of intellectual knowledge and kinesthetic skill are very different. Translating basic understanding into advanced application under performance conditions requires months and years of practice.

What comes after the Level One course in Estill Voice Training: Figures for Voice Control? Students may move directly into study of Level Two: Figure Combinations for Six Voice Qualities, or they may choose to invest some time working on the Level One Figures. In the latter case, here are some suggestions:

- Practice Figures for a few minutes every day

- Practice with purpose
  Organize your practice, and concentrate on one or two Figures each day. The choice is up to you: cycle through the *Figures in a Flash* randomly, practice the easy Figures to build your confidence, or focus on the more challenging ones!

- Find "Practice Partners"
  Practice with other participants in the voice studio or Level One course attended. Working in groups is fun, and shared successes are motivating. Ask your instructor about practice groups in your area, internet forums where you can connect with others working on their Figures.

- Check in with an Estill Master Trainer or Estill Mentor and Course Instructor
  Take a lesson or have a consultation with someone who is qualified to answer questions and coach you through the toughest Figures. A list is available on *estillvoice.com*.

- Purchase and work with *Estill Voiceprint Plus*
  This sound analysis program is available from Estill Voice Internationa at *estillvoice.com*.

- Learn more about the anatomy
  On the last page of this booklet is a list of references used in the preparation of this text; however, almost any anatomy or speech and hearing text will be useful in these early stages of study. Visit a local library.

- Take another Level One Course. Most people find a second time around on this material and these exercises is very useful, whether it is a specific "review course" or not.

- Take a Level Two Course. For those who favor "top – down" information processing, it is just possible that working in Qualities will assist in refining understanding and implementation of the Figures in Level One.

Know that it is perfectly normal to have questions and to feel insecure in performance of the Figures after an initial Level One Course – especially if this has been in context of a 3 Day Course. Most Certified Course Instructors and Certified Masters willingly admit that it took them 3 weeks, 3 months, or even 3 *years* to reach the point where they felt competent in certain aspects of the Estill Voice Model.

Estill Voice International wishes you success in achieving your vocal goals.

REFERENCES

As noted in the Acknowledgement, much of the Figure text and nearly all of the exercises are drawn from the following sources:

Estill, J. (1988). *(The Shiki Papers) A Set of Compulsory Figures for the Master Voice Technician in Speaking, Acting, or Singing.* New York City.

Estill, J. (1992). *Basic Figures and Exercise Manual.* New York City: Imagetech.

Estill, J. (1995). *VOICECRAFT: A User's Guide to Voice Quality. Volume Two: Some Basic Voice Qualities.* Santa Rosa, California: Estill Voice Training Systems.

Estill, J. (1996). *Primer of Compulsory Figures: Level One.* Santa Rosa, California: Estill Voice Training Systems.

Estill, J. (1997). *Primer of Compulsory Figures, Level Two: Six Basic Voice Qualities.* Santa Rosa, California: Estill Voice Training Systems.

Estill, J. (1997-2000). *Level One: Primer of Basic Figures.* Santa Rosa, California: Estill Voice Training Systems.

Estill, J. (2003). *Primer of Compulsory Figures: Level One, Revised Edition.* Santa Rosa, California: Estill Voice Training Systems.

Additional References:

Ackand, R.D. (1999). *Video Atlas of Human Anatomy, Tape 4: The Head and Neck, Part 1.* Baltimore, Maryland: Lippincott Williams & Wilkins.

Estill, J. (1997). *A Programmed Introduction: Anatomy of the Vocal Instrument.* Santa Rosa, California: Estill Voice Training Systems.

Gray, H. (1974). *Anatomy, Descriptive and Surgical, 1901 Edition.* Philadelphia, Pennsylvania: Running Press.

Hirano, M. (1974). Morphological structure of the vocal cord as a vibrator and its variations. Folia Phoniatrica, 26. 89-94.

Kelso, J.A.S. (1995). *Dynamic Patterns: The Self Organization of Brain and Behavior.* Cambridge, MA: MIT Press.

Kent, R. D. & Read, C. (1992). *The Acoustic Analysis of Speech.* San Diego, California: Singular Publishing Group.

McMinn, R.M.H., Hutchings, R.T. & Logan, B.M. (1981). *Color Atlas of Head and Neck Anatomy.* Chicago, Illinois: Year Book Medical Publishers.

McWilliams, B.J., Morris, H.L. & Shelton, R.L. (1990) *Cleft Palate Speech.* Philadelphia, Pennsylvania: B.C. Decker, Inc.

Netter, F. H. (1997). *Atlas of Human Anatomy, Second Edition.* East Hanover, New Jersey: Novartis.

Shriberg, L.D. & Kent, R.D. (1982). *Clinical Phonetics.* New York, New York: Macmillan

Seikel, J., King, D.W., & Drumright, D. G. (1997). *Anatomy and Physiology for Speech, Language, and Hearing.* San Diego, London: Singular Publishing Group.

Stevens, S.S. (1957). On the psychophysical law. *Psychological Review*, 64: 153-181.

Titze, I. (1994). *Principles of Voice Production.* Englewood Cliffs, New Jersey: Prentiss Hall.

Vennard, W. (1967). *SINGING the Mechanism and the Technic.* New York City: Carl Fischer.

Wallace, S.A. (1996). Dynamic pattern perspective of rhythmic movement: An introduction. In H.N. Zelaznik (Ed.) *Advances in Motor Learning and Control* (155-194). Champaign, IL: Human Kinetics

Zemlin, W.R. (1988). *Speech and Hearing Science: Anatomy and Physiology, 3rd Edition.* New Jersey: Prentice Hall.

Research Videos

Yanagisawa, E., Estill, J. & Kmucha, S.T. (1988). *The Contribution of Aryepiglottic Constriction to "Ringing" Voice Quality.*

Yanagisawa, E., Kmucha, S.T. & Estill, J. (1989). *The Role of the Soft Palate in Laryngeal Function and in Selected Voice Qualities.*

Yanagisawa, E., Mambrino, L., Estill, J. & Talkin, D. (1990). *Supraglottic Contributions to Pitch Raising.*

Yanagisawa, E., Mambrino, L., Estill, J. & Talkin, D. (1991). *The Voluntary Control of the Soft Palate.*

Estill, J. & Yanagisawa, E. (1991). *Laryngeal Constriction and Its Retraction.*

Yanagisawa, E., Citardi, M. & Estill, J. (1995). *The Laughing Larynx.*